Title: Amazônia Brasil
Script and Texts: Eugênio Scannavino Netto
Cover: Gringo Cardia | Photo Luis Claudio Marigo
Art Direction, Exposition and Book Design: Gringo Cardia
Production Coordinator: Mesosfera (Gringa Cardia) I Fare Arte
Graphic Design Coordinator: Gleise Cruz
Graphic Designers Assistants: Carolina Vaz and Gabriel Caymmi
Research Coordinator: José Arnaldo de Oliveira
Iconography Research: Isabel Gnaccarini and Janaina Pissinato
Scientific Research Assistant: Gloria Malavoglia
Technical Colaborators: Carlos Roberto Bueno | INPA and João Meirelles Filho | Peabiru
Marcos Roberto Pinheiro | WWF, Adriana Ramos | ISA, Paulo Adário | Greenpeace
Adalberto Veríssimo | Imazon and Caetano Scannavino Filho | PSA, Antonio Donato Nobre | INPE
Translation Coordinator: Melanie Wyffels
Editing: Myrna Schlegel, Gloria Gardner, Peter Jabin
Printing: Gráfica Van Moorsel

Printed in Couché Suzano® Matte from Suzano Papel
e Celulose, produced from renewable eucalyptus forest.
The trees utilized to produce this paper have been
planted for this purpose.

Netto, Eugênio Scannavino; Oliveira, José Arnaldo de
Amazônia Brasil/ Eugênio Scannavino Netto and José Arnaldo de Oliveira;
translation Melanie Wyffels. – São Paulo: Amazonia.Br, 2008
Original title: Amazônia Brasil
ISBN 978-85-61470-00-5
1. Environment 2. Brazil - Amazon

AmAZÔnia BrASil

"We dedicate this work to the forest communities and
the anonymous heroes who everyday defend the Amazonia
and our planet, often at the cost of their own lives"

Eugenio Scannavino Netto and José Arnaldo de Oliveira

Tropical forests are among the most complex of ecosystems. However, they are one of the least known natural systems and therefore very susceptible to human intervention.

"...I am a son of the ancient Yanomamis, I live in the forest where my people have lived since I was born and I don't tell white men that I discovered it!
It has always been here, before me.
I don't say: 'I discovered the sky!' I don't say:
'I discovered the fish, I discovered hunting!'
They were always there from the beginning of time.
I simply say that they are part of life, just like me. That's all."

Davi Kopenawa Yanomami

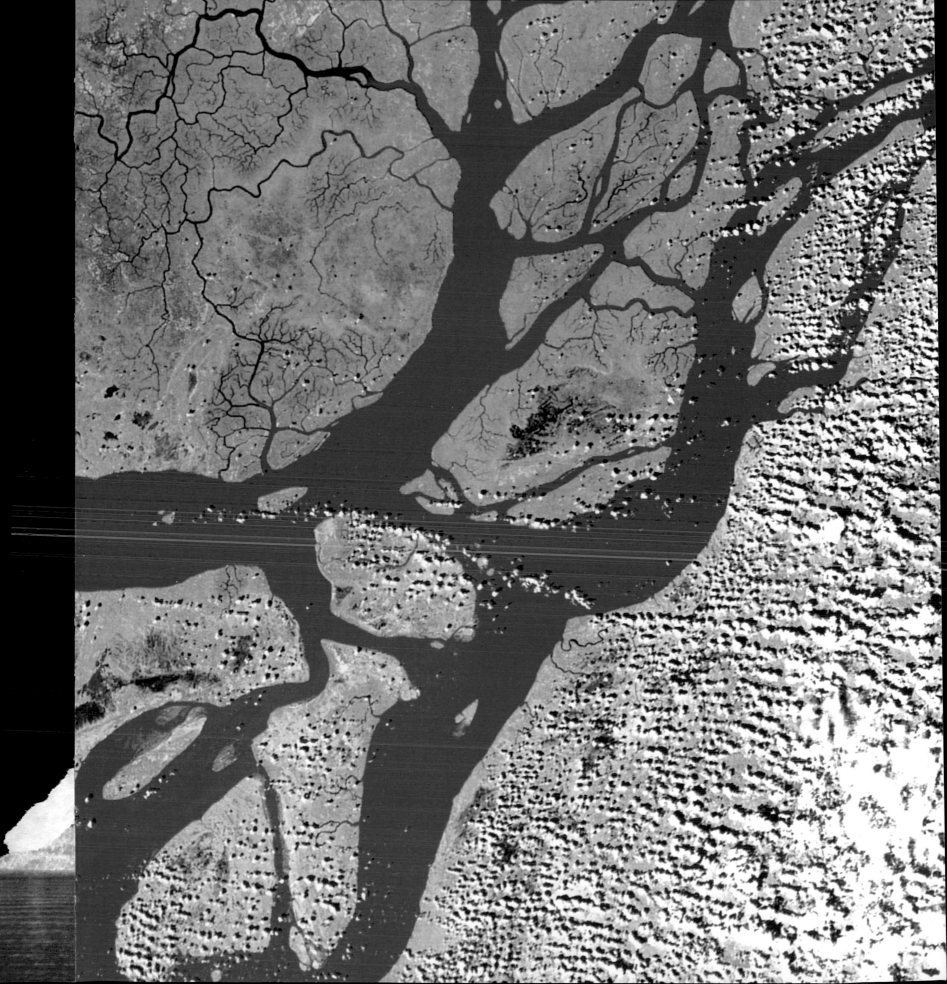

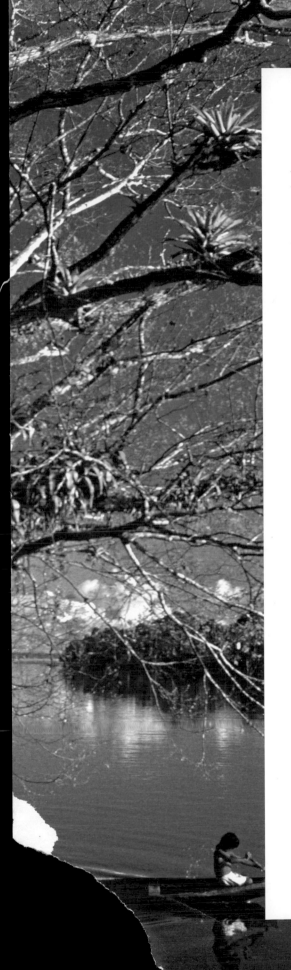

Presentation

Amazon is one of the world's most well known names. However, very little is known about its reality, the circumstances of its population and existing positive enterprises.

A lot is heard about the destruction of the region, but few are aware of the many transforming and successful initiatives currently underway, initiatives based on sustainable development, preservation and conservation of the environment and respect for the culture and customs of the peoples of the forest.

A realistic and long term strategy for preserving the environment and for sustainable development in the Amazon necessarily depends on promoting existing positive experiences, especially those developed by the traditional and extractive communities who live there.

These communities defend their natural forests and culture as best they can, because they depend upon them for their survival. Most of them are still isolated and almost unknown, significantly lacking in technical and material resources.

They need all the support we can offer in order to be strengthened to play an effective transformative role.

The difficulties are as great as the region's magnitude, but we continue to dedicate all our efforts towards creating the greatest amount of benefits possible, together with other organizations like ours, community friends and partners from other regions, to whom we are very grateful.

Over the past 20 years, it has been our great privilege to be able to work both in the Amazon and with the communities of the Amazon. We have learned a lot.

We have been delighted by children's smiles. The purity, the spontaneous joy, and the wisdom of these communities, as well as the immensity of the internal and the external environment of these forest peoples have moved us.

We would like to share with you just a little of these collective efforts and hidden treasures.

Eugênio Scannavino Netto

Health and Happiness Project
Coordinator and Director of Amazônia Brasil

Alcoa and the Amazon

Alcoa is a Values-based Company. Its seven Values – Integrity, People, Client, Environment, Health and Safety, Accountability, Excellence and Profitability – bind together 100,000 Alcoans across 44 nations around the world. These Values constitute the foundations of this 120 year-old Company's strong commitment to Sustainability, best expressed by the "triple bottom-line" of economic success, social progress and environmental excellence.

In the early 1990's a Strategic Framework for 2020 was defined, which translates Alcoa's concern about the state of our planet, and its future, into quantifiable targets. More recently, amongst other initiatives in this same realm, our Company became a prime mover in the formation of USCAP - United States Climate Action Partnership, a group of corporations and environmental organizations that calls on the US Federal Government to quickly enact strong national legislation to significantly reduce greenhouse gas emissions.

It is because of this concern – and, more importantly, because of the actions and practices it has adopted to live its Values and to incorporate Sustainability as a part of its business strategy – that Alcoa has been often recognized as a global leader in corporate responsibility. It has been a member, over the years, of the Dow Jones Sustainability Index, and consistently nominated as the most ethical mining and metals company in the ranking of Covalence, a Swiss organization that measures the institutional reputation of global companies – and these are only two of the important recognitions received by Alcoa due to its commitment to Sustainability.

With a long-term successful presence in Brazil – and particularly in the Amazon region – Alcoa recognizes that the Amazon is a global icon of our need to protect our planet, our climate, our biodiversity, while fostering the development of those who live there. Not because this is fashionable, but because it is an inescapable duty, if we wish future generations to prosper.

An important part of this responsibility is, of course, helping to increase the entire planet's awareness of the need to allow the Amazon to harmonize its economic development, environmental conservation and the improvement of the life quality of its more than 20 million inhabitants.

Consistent with our commitment to Sustainability, and with our conviction of the Amazon's critical value to our and future lives on this Earth, Alcoa is proud and honored to offer the American public and foreign tourists in New York "Amazonia Brasil", this unique Amazonic experience, which now arrives in the city that embodies the heart of the American continent and of the responsible world.

Franklin L. Feder
President
Alcoa Latin America and Caribbean

Amazonia on the Planet

1

Human civilization has destroyed 80% of the world's native forests, mainly in the temperate zones.

It occupies **5% of the planet's surface** (7.9 million km^2 / 3.05 million sq mi)

• Continental Amazon represents over 60% of the planet's remaining tropical forests (in 80 countries)

• It is the planet's last great continuous area of tropical forests.

• The Amazon contains the planet's greatest depository of biodiversity. It is home to approximately 25% of all the world's identified plant and animal species.

• The Amazon Basin is the largest in the planet, with over 7 thousand tributaries.

• It accounts for 20% of all the water flowing into the ocean from rivers on the planet.

• It produces 20 billion tons of water vapor a day, regulating humidity and winds in South America and the world's climate.

The South American Amazon

WWF, IBAMA

The Amazon sprawls over Brazil, Colombia, Ecuador, Guyana and French Guyana, Peru, Surinam and Venezuela.

The Continental Amazon occupies more than half of the South American territory, lying between the Andes Mountain Range in the west and the Atlantic Ocean in the east.

15

The Brazilian ^{2} Amazon

Amazon occupies **61%** of the **national territory**

(5,217,423 km2 / 2,014,295 sq mi)

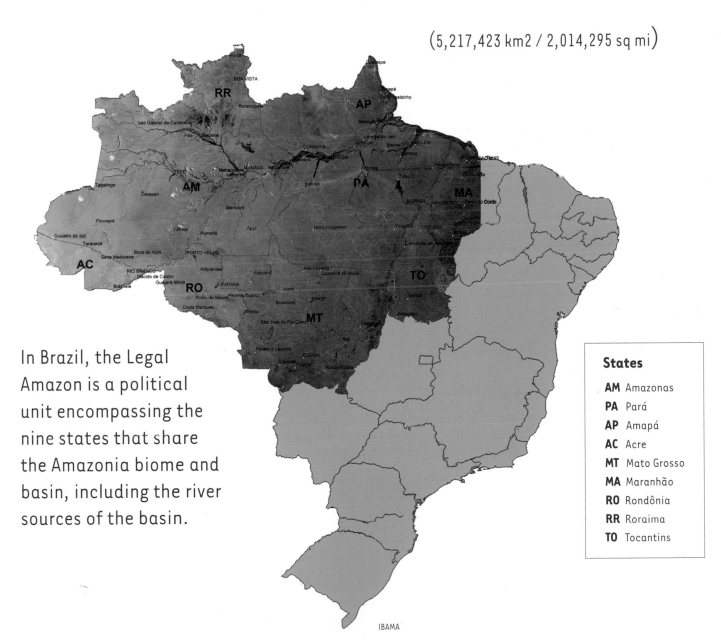

In Brazil, the Legal Amazon is a political unit encompassing the nine states that share the Amazonia biome and basin, including the river sources of the basin.

States

AM Amazonas
PA Pará
AP Amapá
AC Acre
MT Mato Grosso
MA Maranhão
RO Rondônia
RR Roraima
TO Tocantins

IBAMA

Amazonia's Diversity

- **25%** of the world's plant and animal species.

- **30 thousand** known plant species.

- **300** catalogued e**dible fruit.**

- **1,200 birds** species.

- **324 mammalian** species.

- The region is home to **23 million people** from diverse **ethnic** and **cultural origins.**

- **3 million** people live in communities **in the forest.**

- **180 indigenous** peoples.

- Development in the Amazon has often been a process of accelerated destruction.

  Today the region hosts thousands of local positive initiatives pursuing a sustainable development model.

Scientists believe that only 30% of the species in the Brazilian Amazonia have been identified. There are still many areas that remain untouched by humans and have not yet been studied.

Amazonia is a dynamic, complex and extremely diversified universe. We all need to know and respect this region.

Ecoregions

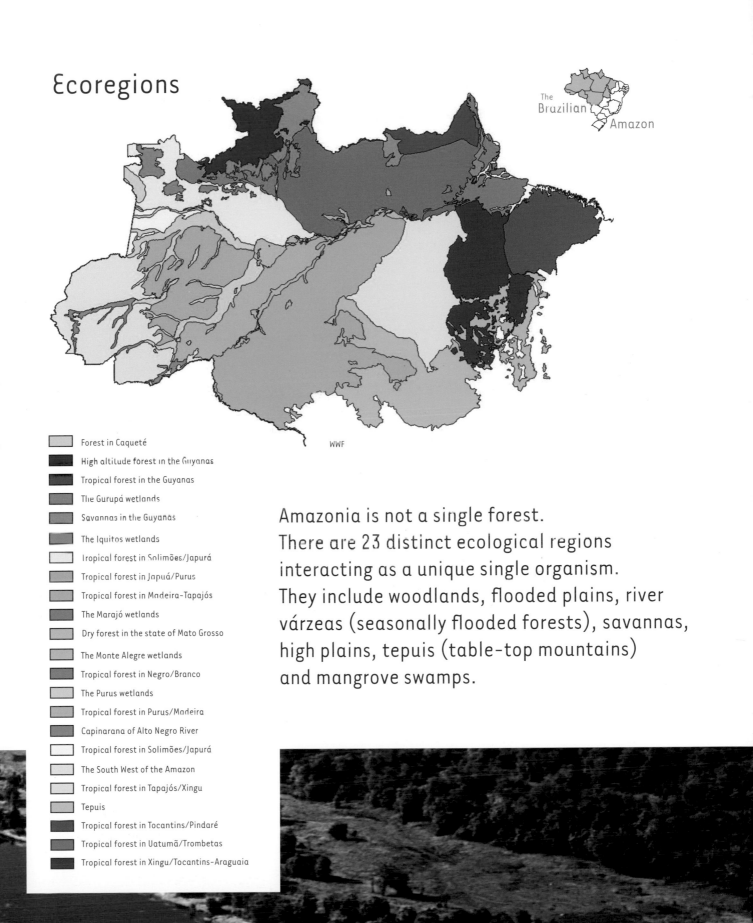

The
Brazilian
Amazon

WWF

Legend:

- Forest in Caqueté
- High altitude forest in the Guyanas
- Tropical forest in the Guyanas
- The Gurupá wetlands
- Savannas in the Guyanas
- The Iquitos wetlands
- Tropical forest in Solimões/Japurá
- Tropical forest in Japuá/Purus
- Tropical forest in Madeira-Tapajós
- The Marajó wetlands
- Dry forest in the state of Mato Grosso
- The Monte Alegre wetlands
- Tropical forest in Negro/Branco
- The Purus wetlands
- Tropical forest in Purus/Madeira
- Capinarana of Alto Negro River
- Tropical forest in Solimões/Japurá
- The South West of the Amazon
- Tropical forest in Tapajós/Xingu
- Tepuis
- Tropical forest in Tocantins/Pindaré
- Tropical forest in Uatumã/Trombetas
- Tropical forest in Xingu/Tocantins-Araguaia

Amazonia is not a single forest.
There are 23 distinct ecological regions
interacting as a unique single organism.
They include woodlands, flooded plains, river
várzeas (seasonally flooded forests), savannas,
high plains, tepuis (table-top mountains)
and mangrove swamps.

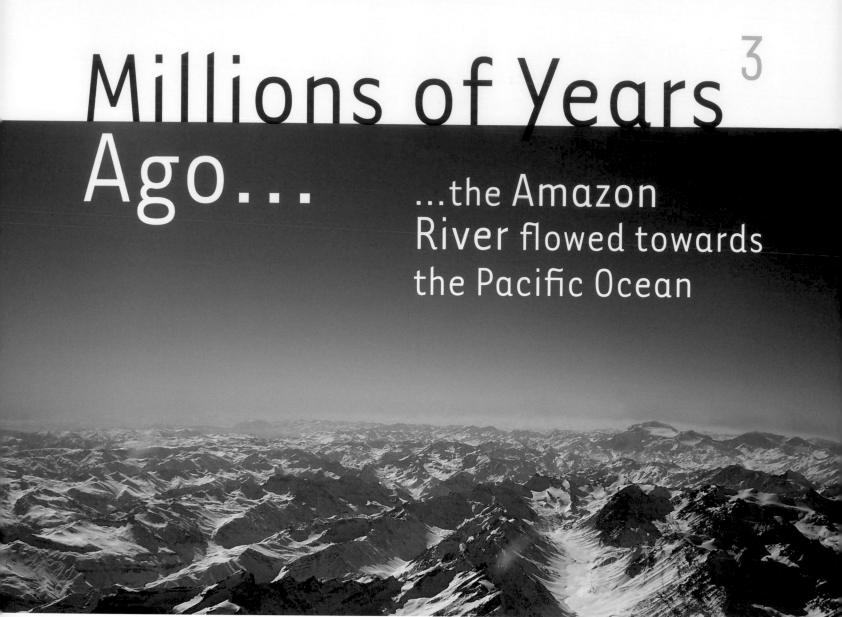

Millions of Years ³ Ago...

...the Amazon River flowed towards the Pacific Ocean

Around 420 million years ago, the Amazon surface was covered by ocean water and formed an open gulf facing the Pacific Ocean. At that time, the Andes Mountain Range had not yet been formed; South America and Africa formed one single continent.

During the subsequent 150 million years, rivers were formed that flowed from east to west towards the Pacific Ocean.

Nearly 70 million years ago the Andes Mountain Range was formed, blocking the water flowing to the west, thus creating lakes and flooded regions. The Amazon River then started to drain towards the Atlantic Ocean.

The Tepuis

Tepuis, tabletop mountains surrounded by forests and savannas, are one of the oldest rock formations in South America. They form a "corridor" at the borders of the Amazonia in Brazil, the Guyanas and Venezuela.

It is estimated that this geological formation was formed approximately 2 billion years ago and hosts seven times as many endemic species than anywhere else on the continent.

This ancient place inspired Sir Arthur Conan Doyle's novel "The Lost World".

Pico da Neblina

Covered by clouds at its summit throughout most of the year, Pico da Neblina is one of the highest mountains in Brazil (3,014 m/9,842 ft).

Located near the Brazil-Venezuela border, the temperature varies from 12 c to 34°C / 53.6 to 93.2° F.

The region has inspired many indigenous myths and only recently have scientific studies of the region begun.

Stingray

This geological history can be verified by the fact that the Amazonian stingray's (*Potamotrygon* spp) intestinal parasites are the same as those found in the Pacific Ocean rays.

Hydrographic Basin [4]

Boats

Over 100 thousand different kinds of vessels serve as buses and trucks.

Approximately 23,000 km / 14,291 miles of rivers create navigational routes that are the real "roads" in the Amazon. Many communities and cities are accessible only by water.

The Amazon Basin has seven thousands tributaries and drains an area of 584.6 million hectares.

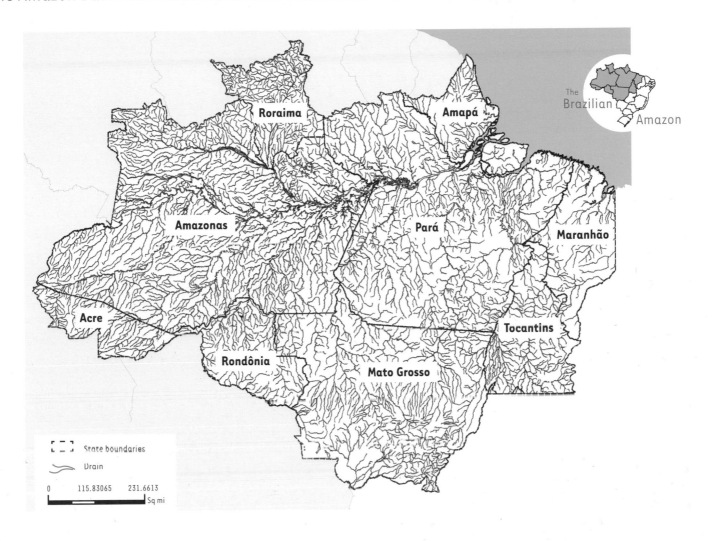

The Amazon River

The outflow from the Amazon Basin accounts for one-fifth of all the fresh water flowing into the oceans.

From its source in the Andes to its estuary, the river is 6,857 km / 4,261 miles long, comparable to the distance between Berlin and New York.

Recent studies confirm that the Amazon River has the highest water outflow and is also the world's longest river (179 km / 111 miles longer than the Nile).

In Brazil, the Amazon River descends only 80 m / 262 ft to sea level.

"Amazonia is an ocean of forests in an ocean of fresh water"

Avé-Lallemant in *Rio Amazonas*, 1859

"The rivers in Amazonia command our lives"

Leandro Tocantins

The Amazon Estuary

The mouth of the main stream is over 250 km / 155 miles wide and it outpours into the ocean for a distance of about 150 km / 93 miles.

One flow second of the Amazon River (approximately 175 millions liters / 46,230,109 gallons of water per second) is enough to supply water to a city of 2,000,000 inhabitants for an entire day.

Marajó Island

The extensive Marajó Island, located at the mouth of the Amazon River, is the size of Switzerland (50,000 km^2 / 19,305 sq mi). Beaches, mangroves, buffalos and extensive palm forests can be found in the region. It is also known for its elaborate archeological ceramic pottery.

Pororoca

The ocean waters roll up the Amazon River generating violent waves; this phenomenon is known as the pororoca.

Surfing the pororoca has become a popular sport; the phenomenon can last up to 40 minutes.

MACAPÁ

BELÉM

SÃO LUI

Mangroves

The waters of the Amazon, along with the ocean, form the largest continuous mangrove belt on the planet, covering an area of of 8,386 km^2 / 3,237 sq mi. It is an important reproductive area for many Atlantic Ocean species.

This coast is also comprised of flooded forests, swamps, beaches and water containing unique species.

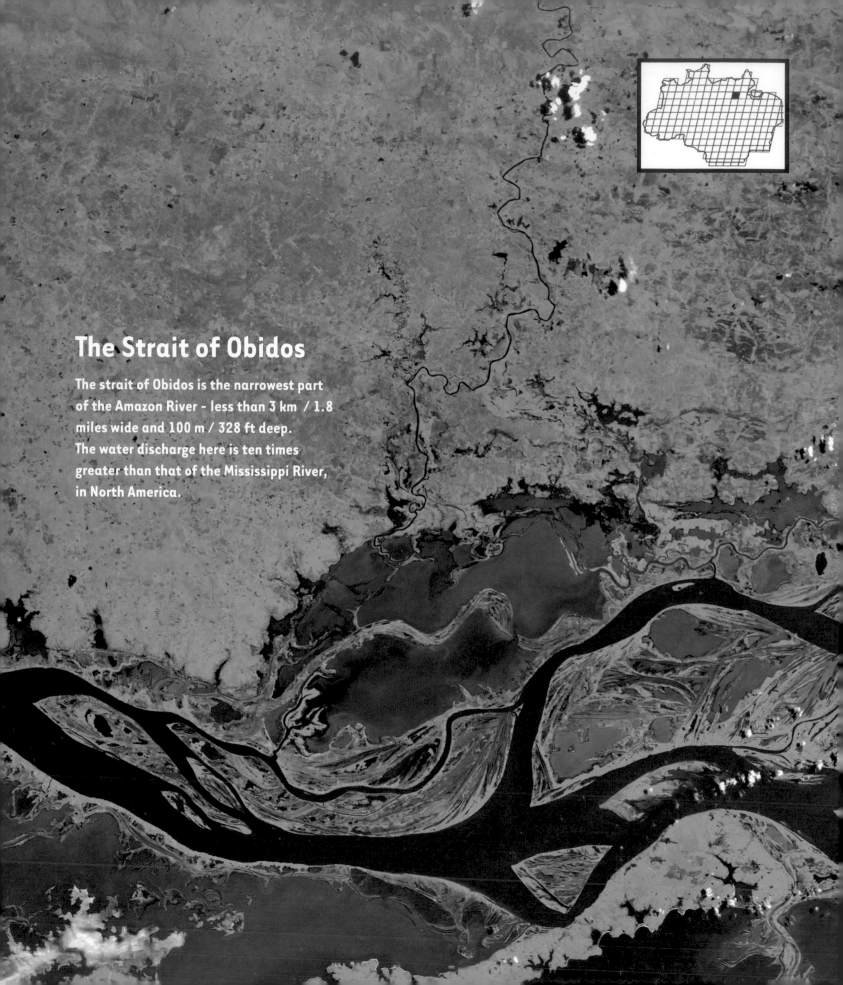

The Strait of Obidos

The strait of Obidos is the narrowest part
of the Amazon River - less than 3 km / 1.8
miles wide and 100 m / 328 ft deep.
The water discharge here is ten times
greater than that of the Mississippi River,
in North America.

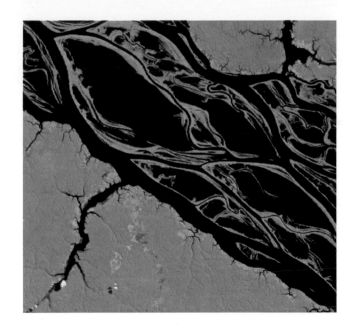

Anavilhanas

The Negro River forms one of the world's largest fluvial archipelagos: Anavilhanas. Here the river can be 24 km / 14.9 mile wide. In the Brazilian territory, the Negro River is 1200 km / 745.64 miles long, and descends at a rate of only 5.5 cm / 2.2 inches per mile.

The Tidal Bore

Different water density, composition and temperature keep the Solimões and Negro rivers flowing separately for 6 km / 3.7 miles before they finally join to form the great Amazon.

Types of Water

Biological and geological characteristics of the Amazon region form three main types of water — muddy, green and black. This diversity is a result of the presence of different sediments and minerals in the water.

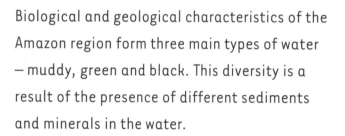

White Water (Muddy or Clear)	White water rivers drain from the Andes and flow towards the Atlantic Ocean. Tons of sediment are washed into the rivers, which explains the color of their waters.	River margins have fertile soil and fish are abundant. High diversity of fish species is found in great numbers.	Amazonas, Juruá, Purus, Madeira, Trombetas, Acre Rivers, among others
Dark or Black waters	Rivers that flow through geologically old, sandy areas. Their waters run through flooded forests, where organic material rapidly decomposes, thus darkening the color of the waters.	Rivers have many different fish species but fish population is small.	Negro, Urubu, Uatumã, Rivers, among others
Clear Water Greenish/Blue waters	Many clear water rivers, which run from south to north, have their source in the Central Highlands. They flow through ancient rocks and their margins are high and stable.	Fish population is larger than in black water rivers, and smaller than in clear water rivers.	Tapajós, Guaporé, Xingu, Rivers, among others.

Water Cycles

The water system of the Amazon follows two main seasons: the wet season and the dry season. River levels vary as much as 15 m / 49.2 ft and in some places the width of the river varies more than 20 km / 12.4 miles.

Annual Rainfall Chart

Amazon Forest:

up to 100 in

Temperate Forests:

between 27 to 59 in

Deserts:

0.60 in

Flooded Forests

During the rainy season in winter the rivers in the Amazon overflow their banks into extensive areas, covering over 30 million hectares (6% of the Brazilian Amazon).

The flooded forests are home to the most extraordinary biodiversity. Tons of fertile soil and organic matter from the Andes flow into the river waters.

During the dry season, in summer, the waters recede and open space for fertile lands that are used as natural pasture or agriculture.

During this period, river margins become sandy beaches. With limited hiding space, fish become easy prey.

Life in riverside communities depends greatly on the flooded forests; these areas also supply fish for consumption in larger cities and for export.

The Amazon River in the wet season (1) and dry season (2)

Flooded Igapó Forests

During the wet season, riverbeds overflow and cover forests, forming the 'igapós'.
Some trees are submerged for up to six months, creating a unique environment where fish feed on
trapped insects and mammals. Many trees have breathing roots and drift seeds.

Victoria Amazonica

The Victoria-Regia's (Royal water lily) leaves grow up to 40 inches in diameter, and can
hold the weight of a small child.

The Amazon basin is a repository of fish:
1,400 identified species, comprising
25% of the world's known fish species.

Aquatic Animals 5

Fish

Fish are the single most significant source of protein and the core staple in the diet of the riverside population, (annual average consumption of 60 kg / 132 lb per capita).

Pirarucu

The largest species of Brazilian scaled fish, the pirarucu (*Arapaima gigas*) grows up to 3 m / 9.8 ft in length and weighs up to 881 lb. Fossils approximately 200 million years old have been found.

For centuries, indigenous people have used the pirarucus' bony hard tongue to grate the bark and fruit of the guaraná plant for medicinal purposes. Previously threatened, this species is now reproducing due to successful management programs.

The pirarucu is capable of aerial respiration, and the substances found in its gills are extremely valuable in the research market (prices can reach $5 per milligram).

Poraquê

Commonly known as the electric eel, this feared species (Gymnotiformes) sends out electrical pulses to guide itself and to attack its prey. With shocks of up to 600 volts they can paralyze or knock their food off aquatic trees (insects, fruits, seeds).

They also use electrical pulses to communicate with each other.

Accidents involving humans are frequent.

The electric eel is the focus of projects for electrical monitoring of the waters.

Piranha

Piranhas are not as aggressive as some stories suggest. They only attack
in situations of extreme confinement (in small lakes during droughts) and when
they are hungry. Piranhas don't pose any risk during river bathing. According
to local folklore, the piranha soup has aphrodisiac powers.

Serrasalmus spp

Phractocephalus hemioliopterus

Catfish

The large Amazonian Catfish (Siluriformes) migrate 5,000 km / 3,106 miles to reproduce, from the mouth of the Amazon to its source in the Andes. The largest is the Piraíba (*Brachyplatystoma filamentosum*), which has been reported to grow over 2.5 m / 8.2 ft and weigh up to 200 kg / 440 lb.

Ornamental Fish

The Amazon is home to approximately 2,000 identified species of the most beautiful ornamental fish. Over 20 million ornamental fish from a few targeted species are captured annually in precarious condition; many are exported illegally.

When buying an ornamental fish try to know its origin and certification.

Manatee

The Amazonian manatee (*Trichechus inunguis*) occurs exclusively in freshwater. It weighs up to 480 kg / 992 lb and can ingest 50 kg / 110 lb of vegetation a day. This peaceful mammal is currently threatened with extinction.

Aquatic Mammals

Dolphins

The Amazon dolphin (*Inia geoffrensis*), or boto, is a freshwater version of the marine dolphin.

Botos can vary in color and size: from a memorable bright pink color, or red, to a murky brown or gray, known as tucuxi. The pink boto is larger and more agile, whereas the gray boto is smaller and swims rapidly.

The pink boto has the most flexible skeleton among the cetaceans, which gives it maneuverability in the flooded forests.

The boto is surrounded by many legends in the Amazon region. One legend has it that at night a boto becomes a handsome young man - with a hat to cover his respiratory orifice - who seduces girls in the forest during nocturnal festivities. Children born out of wedlock are sometimes said to be the boto's offspring - and botos are sometimes the registered fathers!

The Giant Otter

The giant otter (*Petronura brasiliensis*) is an aquatic mammal, of the sea otter family. They can grow up to 5.9 ft in length and weigh 66 lb. Although hunted almost to extinction for their pelts sold in the European market, they are now a protected species.

Reptiles and amphibians

Caiman

Caimans can grow up to 6 m / 19.6 ft in length (*Melanosuchus niger*) and can have a life span of 100 years. Unlike crocodiles (that don't occur in the Amazon), caimans rarely attack human beings — in fact, few attacks have been registered in the last 15 years. However, accidents between fishermen and caimans are more frequent.

Its population has been severely depleted due to commercial hunting for the international leather industries. Today, however, the caiman population has recovered.

Jacaré-Açú

Jacaretinga

Tracajá

The Amazonian Turtle

Among the numerous chelonians, the Amazonian turtle (*Podocnemis expansa*) is the largest river turtle in South America and can measure up to 1 m / 3.2 ft in length.

Between 1700 and 1900, the international market consumed 214 million turtles for their oil, used in outdoor lighting, butter and medicinal salves.

The female turtles lay their eggs on the beaches during the dry season.

Protection plans and control measures have helped increase the population of the turtle.

Anaconda/Sucuri

The Sucuri (*Eunectes murinus*), or Anaconda, can grow to 10 m/32 ft in length, twice the size of a compact car.

For a single meal, it can swallow an animal the size of a pig.

Amazonia is home to over 300 known species of snakes.

Frogs

Brazil is home to the most varieties of frogs in the world.

The Amazon has 163 known and catalogued amphibious species. However, this figure is likely much higher, since only few navigable rivers have been researched.

The cururu frog (*Bufo marinus*) is 30 cm / 11.8 inches in length and can weigh up to 1 kg / 2.2 lb.

Some are extremely toxic and secrete substances that have been traditionally used in indigenous medicine. The value and complexity of such substances are now being studied and understood by the scientists.

Amphibians are extraordinarily sensitive to environmental changes and water contamination.

Dendrobates leucomelas

Terra Firma
Forest

An estimated 200
thousand plant species

One single tree can grow up to 55 m / 60 yards in height (equivalent to a 20-story building). Many trees grow six times faster than those in temperate zones.

A tree can host approximately 1,700 species of invertebrate.

There are more tree species in an average hectare of the Amazon forest than in all of Europe and North America.

Fruits

There are over 300 identified edible fruits (cupuaçu, açai, guaraná and others) in the Amazon - a small fraction, actually, of all the fruits eaten by animals that participate in the renewal of the cycles of nature.

Seeds

One of the great Amazonian wonders is the diversity in forms, sizes, colors and dissemination strategies of the seeds, where the plant life begins. Forest peoples use seeds as food, medicine and in handicrafts. In the reforestation process, some of the seeds from the highest trees require similar harvesting techniques as in rappelling.

When buying forest products try to know its origin and certification.

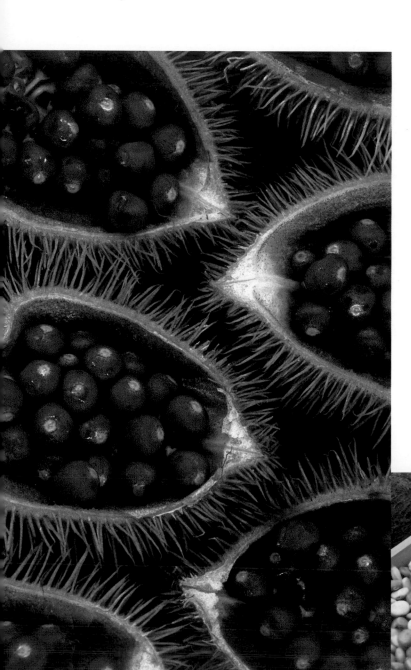

Palm Trees

Palm trees (Palmaceae) are very common in the Brazilian Amazon. They are very important for both animals and local human communities. Different types of fruit and nuts produce oils that are used to manufacture soap and wines.

Heart of palm, or palmito, found in the upper tip of the palm tree, has extremely valuable culinary uses and is widely exported.

The tastiest palmito comes from the açaí palm, which also produces the internationally renowned açaí fruit.

Fibers and leaves of the palm trees are used in handicrafts and for building materials.

Forest Vines

Tropical vines give the forests a dense appearance and form 'highways' for the Amazon wildlife (monkeys, sloths, insects, birds, etc.)

Some vines store and provide fresh clean water to the indigenous people during their long journeys.

Vines are used in traditional medicine, handicrafts, construction of huts and furniture. An average use cycle of 4 years benefits the sustainable use of vines.

Terrestrial
Animals 7

Macacos-de-cheiro (*Saimiri sciureus*)

Mammals

There are over 324 mammalian species in Amazonia.

Jaguars

The jaguar (*Panthera onca*) has the most powerful bite among felines.

There are different types of jaguars: the spotted, the black and the brown.

Monkeys

The Amazon has more varieties of monkeys than any other region of the planet.

There are approximately 100 species and since 1990 an average of one new species is discovered every year.

"New species every year"

In 2008, Jean-Phillipe Boubli of the University of Auckland and native Yanomami people identified a new monkey species near Pico da Neblina.

The discovery had the support of Auckland University, New Zealand and the Ministry of Science and Technology of Brazil.

The new monkey was named *Cacajao ayresii* after the Brazilian biologist José Márcio Ayres, who was a pioneer on sustainable development reserves with Mamirauá Institute for Sustainable Development.

Uacari de cara vermelha (*Cacajao calvus*)

Sloths

Sloths (*Bradypus variegatus*) are a walking ecological system.

In one single sloth, scientists have found and catalogued three new species of beetles, six species of ticks and three species of moths.

In another, they found over 900 beetles, a mouse's nest and several invertebrate species.

Tapirs

The tapir (*Tapirus terrestris*),
relative of the rhinoceros family,
is the world's largest rodent.

It can grow up to 2 m / 6.5 ft in length
and weigh up to 200 kg / 440 lb.

Anteaters

The giant anteater, (*Myrmecophaga tridactyla*) is a toothless mammal.

It is known for its keen sense of smell: 40 times more efficient than humans.

With its powerful claws and sticky tongue to trap insects, it can eat over 30 thousand insects in a single day.

It has been listed as an endangered species.

Birds

Amazonia is home to the world's largest concentration of birds: over 1,200 species have been currently identified. However, there may be many more species that have not been recorded; this number may increase with the new sound-analysis technologies that identify song variations and DNA tests.

Fun fact

The survival of the Brazilian rosewood (*Aniba rosaeodora*), which produces the essential oil used as the main ingredient of the Channel No. 5 perfume, greatly relies on the toucans to disperse the seeds after feeding on the fruit.

Toucans

The toucan (*Ramphastos* spp), and its many subspecies, is recognized by the long, colorful bill it uses to feed on fruit and seeds. They usually travel in small flocks and often invade the nests of other birds.

Harpy Eagle

The most majestic of all Amazon birds, the harpy eagle (*Harpia harpyja*) has a wingspan of 2 m / 6.5 ft. It has the most powerful claws of its species. Adults in the villages are sometimes seen picking up their small children when the eagles are seen flying around.

Ara chloropterus

Scarlet Macaw

Macaws are known for their colorful feathers and are very noisy. They live in pairs, feed on fruit and seeds and live in holes in the trees.

Their smaller relatives, the green parrots, have been domesticated for centuries because of their ability to imitate the human voice.

Their feathers are greatly valued and used in indigenous adornments.

Brazil has currently banned the commercialization of any handicraft made with feathers.

Magic Bird

The Japiim is a bird known for its ability to imitate the sounds of other animals. To protect the young, they build their nests near active wasp nests.

To many indigenous peoples, the Japiim are the sons of the Sun, and they are believed to have been ancestral hunters who could imitate the sounds of drums, barking dogs or crying babies.

This ability to speak languages other than their own is also used for seduction.

Cacicus cela

Insects

Insects play a determinant role in the balance of the forest; they are responsible for most of the plant pollination, pest control and seed spreading in the Amazon.

Original forests are the insect's natural home; once deforestation takes place the insects take refuge in human buildings.

Paná-paná: group of Pieridae butterflies

Butterflies   The Amazon is home to over 1,400 species of butterflies.

Approximately 260 thousand types of insects reside in the Amazon; only 30% have been scientifically catalogued.

The large Morpho Butterfly is known for its brilliant iridescent blue wings. In fact, they are brown in color - the vivid blue color being the result of an advanced natural technology of light reflection, which has inspired the modern efficient fiber optics.

Emperor Moth

The Emperor Moth (*Thysania agrippina*) is one the world's largest moths. It has a wingspan of up to 30 cm / 11.8 inches, the equivalent of two ballpoint pens laid end-to-end.

Army Ants

Army ants (Eciton) are nomadic in behavior; massive columns actively raid and forage the forest ground and tree trunks. They feed on pretty much anything they find on their foraging raids. With their own bodies tightly close together they form nests and floating bridges over the rivers. When army ant colonies reach riverside communities, the people are often forced to abandon their houses for up to three days.

Mosquitoes

Mosquitoes infest the muddy waters of Amazonia's rivers. However, contrary to popular belief, they are practically nonexistent in black and green waters.

Many mosquitoes in the Amazon are known to transmit endemic diseases – the most common being malaria, yellow fever and leishmaniose.

An increase of just 2° C / approximately 3° F in the global temperature can accelerate the mosquito reproductive cycle by 40%, thus creating serious public health concerns.

Giant Beetle

The giant beetle (*Titanus gigantus*) is 20 cm / 7.8 inches long.

Bees

Over 300 species of bees (Meliponinae), live in specific regions of the Brazilian Amazon.

The social role of the bee is related to its size. Bees produce unique types of honey from regional endemic flowers.

Many Amazonian bees are stingless, and are threatened by the introduction of stinging species from Europe or Africa and by deforestation, as well.

Iguana iguana

Amazonia is home to 2/3 of the world's species of lizards.

From the ground to the canopy

A single tree in the forest forms an interactive ecosystem with other living organisms found below the ground, in decomposing matter on the soil, in tree trunks and canopies.

Human Footprints

Any single footprint on the Amazonia soil affects about 1,600 different microorganisms.

Environmental Services

Forests provide invaluable environmental services: shade, soil protection, water quality and transformation of carbon into different life forms. Although much remains to be studied, the value of genetic biodiversity is inestimable.

An original forest generates life in itself. It is most generous to all populations living within and from its system.

Positive Experiences

INPA — National Institute For Amazonian Research

One of the centers of excellence in research in the Amazon. It was created in 1954, and is internationally recognized. Its areas of study include biology, forestry, agriculture, health, food and human sciences, and the Forest Fragments Biological Dynamics Project.
www.inpa.gov.br

Emílio Goeldi Museum of Pará

Founded in 1871 in Belém do Pará as the first research center of the Amazon. It is one of the main scientific resources of the region, with activities in the areas of humanities and natural sciences. It is creating the first School of Archeology in the region.
www.museu-goeldi.br

WWF-Brasil

Works on projects that support the protection of biodiversity, sustainable economy and public policies in the Brazilian Amazon.
www.wwf.org.br

Conservation International

Maintains activities concerned with the ecological corridors and protected areas in the Brazilian Amazon.
www.conservation.org.br

Deforestation [8]

83% of the biome is still preserved.

55% is comprised of primary areas; 28% are areas under serious environmental threat.

Since 1970, 17% of the Brazilian Amazon biome has been altered.

An area of 270,271 sq mi — larger than the state of Texas - has been affected in the past 30 years.

The Arch of Deforestation

The swath of deforestation starts in the South/ Southeast and Midwest regions of the country, and continues along the southern and eastern borders of the Amazon.

This area is known as the Arch of Deforestation.

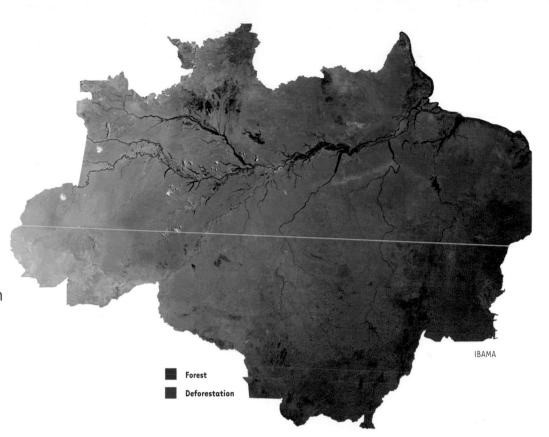

IBAMA

■ Forest

■ Deforestation

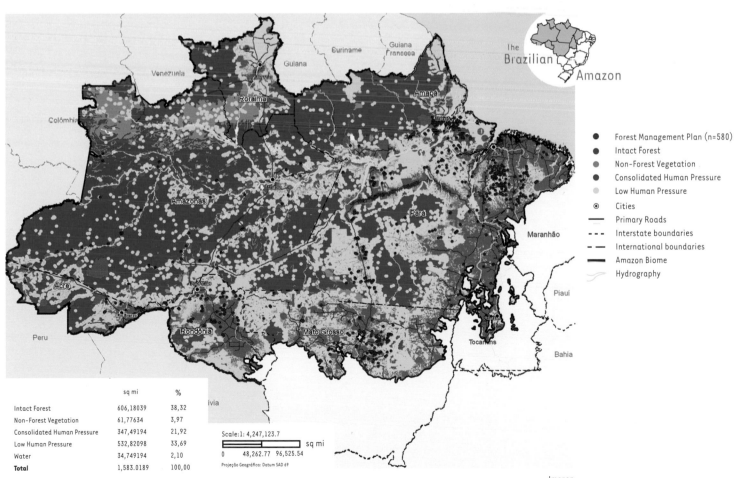

The Brazilian Amazon

- ● Forest Management Plan (n=580)
- ● Intact Forest
- ● Non-Forest Vegetation
- ● Consolidated Human Pressure
- ● Low Human Pressure
- ⊙ Cities
- ── Primary Roads
- --- Interstate boundaries
- ⎯ ⎯ International boundaries
- ── Amazon Biome
- ∿ Hydrography

	sq mi	%
Intact Forest	606,18039	38,32
Non-Forest Vegetation	61,77634	3,97
Consolidated Human Pressure	347,49194	21,92
Low Human Pressure	532,82098	33,69
Water	34,749194	2,10
Total	1,583.0189	100,00

Scale:1: 4,247,123.7

0   48,262.77   96,525.54 sq mi

Projeção Geográfica: Datum SAD 69

The Deforestation Cycle

Context

- Primary forests and local communities
- Surveillance difficulties due to the Amazon's large area
- Socially fragile traditional and indigenous communities
- 75% of public lands lack agrarian reform
- Precarious ecological-economic zoning

Cycle

- Illegal occupation of land and the use of violence
- Biopiracy of natural resources and indigenous knowledge
- Construction of clandestine roads (approximately 107,497 miles)
- Logging of hardwood trees with commercial value
- Use of fire as a clearing practice to illegally occupy pastureland
- Cattle or soy production pushing communities into urban suburbs
- Formation of shantytowns, increase in violence and urban poverty
- The "commodities" market stimulates deforestation of new areas

Positive Experiences

Ministry of the Environment

Coordinates Brazil's environmental policies with the input of all other government areas.

Regulates economic pressures in Amazonia, is responsible for the management of the conservation units and environmental surveillance. Supports and promotes the participation of civil society and traditional peoples in designing its policies.

www.mma.gov.br

Action Plan for Amazon Deforestation Prevention and Control

Federal government plan that congregates 11 ministries and state governments in strategic actions related to environmental inspection, sustainable production and agrarian reforms. This plan has been instrumental to the decrease of deforestation in the Amazon.

www.presidencia.gov.br/casacivil/desmat.pdf

Between 2004 and 2007 there has been a 59% decrease in deforestation in the Brazilian Amazon, representing half of the annual average of 23 thousand km^2 since 1988. However, this is not enough!

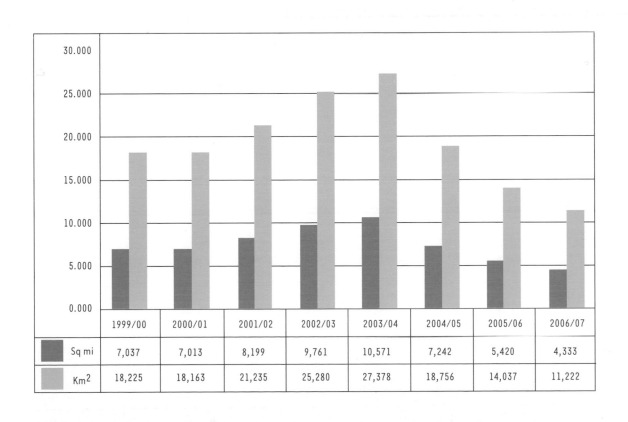

	1999/00	2000/01	2001/02	2002/03	2003/04	2004/05	2005/06	2006/07
Sq mi	7,037	7,013	8,199	9,761	10,571	7,242	5,420	4,333
Km^2	18,225	18,163	21,235	25,280	27,378	18,756	14,037	11,222

Monitoring and Surveillance 9

Strategic
Actions

Integrated Monitoring

Today, with the use of modern satellites, Brazil monitors all predatory activities and environmental crimes in the Amazon region in real time. This system also facilitates swift action in the most remote regions.

The National Institute for Space Research - INPE

Since 1998, this government institution produces annual deforestation rates in the Legal Amazonia. Currently, three monitoring systems cover the region, each with a specific function: PRODES —the Brazilian Amazon Forest Satellite Monitoring; DETER — Real Time Deforestation Detection System, and DETEX — Selective Exploitation Detection.

INPE conducts research related to climate change, which include the observation of the present climate and long-term climate variability, as well as studies projecting future climate scenarios.

www.inpe.br

Amazon Surveillance System — SIPAM

A network of national and sub national public institutions comprised of states and municipalities that carry out governmental activities in the Amazon region. It is comprised of a central office in Brasilia, three operational centers (Pará, Amazonas and Rondônia)and 700 remote terminals.

www.sipam.gov.br

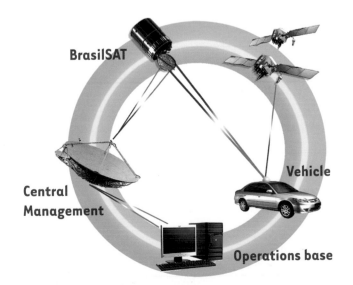

BrasilSAT

Central Management

Vehicle

Operations base

Civil Society Monitors the occupation of the Amazon

The Social-Environmental Institute - ISA

A private institution that promotes and develops projects related to sustainable research; it has one of the largest databases on Brazilian indigenous peoples.

www.socioambiental.org.br

Greenpeace Brasil

Organization that actively promotes campaigns against deforestation, advancement of soy production and climate change in the Amazon.

www.greenpeace.org.br

The Institute of Man and the Environment in the Amazon IMAZON

Studies the occupation of the Amazon and different models for development. It conducts surveys and research concerning the production of wood products from environmental and economic perspectives.

www.Imazon.org.br

Institute of Environmental Research of Amazon (IPAM)

Participates in the strategic analysis of the Amazon and develops practices for sustainable production by families and forforest fire control.

www.ipam.org.br

Friends of the Earth - Brazilian Amazonia

Acts to promote the sustainable use of forest products, the prevention of fire, supporting isolated communities and the development and monitoring of public policies.

www.amazonia.org.br

Surveillance

In 2005 the Amazon Fire Prevention and Deforestation Control Project created nineteen new operational bases to promote a joint surveillance with other federal institutions on environmental matters, which also includes employment, justice, land and taxation.

Detentions due to illegal trafficking of animals, lumber and plants have increased significantly from 2004 to 2007.

1,000,000 cubic meters / 35,314,667 cubic feet of illegal lumber has already been apprehended.

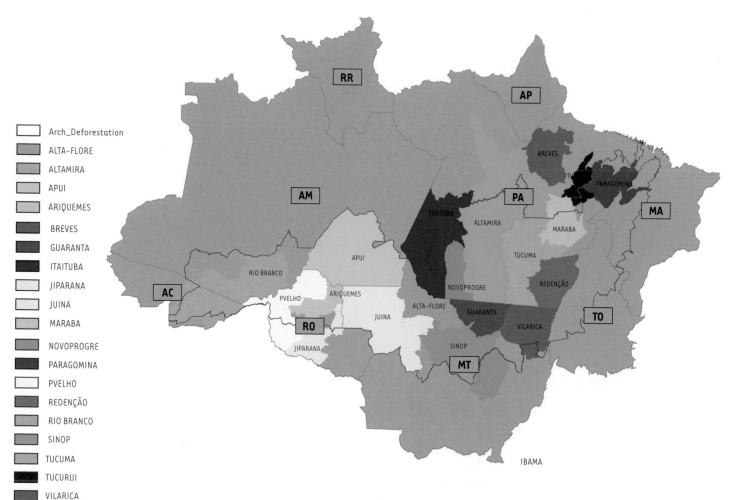

Arch_Deforestation
ALTA-FLORE
ALTAMIRA
APUI
ARIQUEMES
BREVES
GUARANTA
ITAITUBA
JIPARANA
JUINA
MARABA
NOVOPROGRE
PARAGOMINA
PVELHO
REDENÇÃO
RIO BRANCO
SINOP
TUCUMA
TUCURUI
VILARICA

Brazil has the most modern legal Environmental Law in the world; however, surveillance is a difficult challenge due to Amazonia's dimensions and unique natural features.

Borders

The Brazilian Amazon consists of approximately 11,000 km / 6,835 miles of continuous borders with seven countries.

Access is difficult in this immense area that has low population density and is home to transnational indigenous peoples. Besides visitors and local inhabitants the area is also a route for traffickers, foreign guerrillas, missionaries, illegal loggers and miners.

There has been a long standing fear in Brazil regarding the intention of developed countries to "internationalize" Amazonia. Despite the difficulties, territorial defense is a strategic priority of the Brazilian army.

For Brazilians, Brazil's sovereignty over its Amazonian territory is unquestionable, which increases our responsibilities and stresses the importance of excellent governance over this planetary resource.

Military Command of the Amazon

The Brazilian Army, together with the Navy and Air Force, has 62 bases in the Amazon region. It provides support services to the communities and researchers. In partnership with the Federal Police it protects and oversees border areas.
www.exercito.gov.br/06OMs/Comandos/CMA/indice.htm

Positive Experiences

Brazilian Institute for Environment and Natural Renewable Resources - IBAMA

Brazilian agency that implements national environmental policies and promotes the preservation, conservation and sustainable use of environmental resources. It interprets satellite images and informs its site teams as to where environmental offenders are located, thus aiding inspection actions.
www.ibama.gov.br

Federal Police

Responsible for fighting against narcotrafficking, organized crime and public corruption in the country. It also takes actions against deforestation. In the period between 2004 and 2007, over 500 people in Amazonia were arrested.
www.dpf.gov.br

Federal Highway Patrol

Responsible for surveillance of cargo vehicles and has extended action in the interior of Amazonia, restraining illegal and clandestine activities.
www.dprf.gov.br

National Institute for Colonization and Agrarian Reform

Fights against illegal land occupation and regulates communal areas.
www.incra.gov.br

Ranking of the largest deforested areas.

Municipalities with more areas deforested in August – December, 2007.

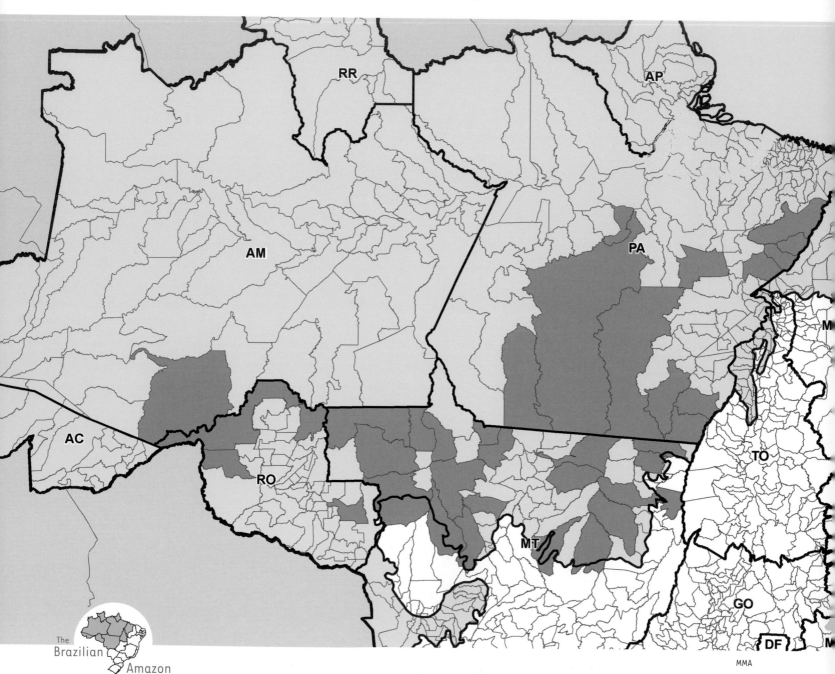

Government Measures

There are 80 thousand rural properties in the municipalities experiencing the highest deforestation rates during this period.

The government has implemented strong measures to contain the deforestation and other illegal actions in these regions. For example, all rural properties must be registered, so that an offending owner can be identified and penalized. A noncompliant property owner will not be able to obtain credit, sell products, sell property, nor obtain receipts or export permits.

Related measures call for the criminal indictment of buyers and consumers of products originating from these properties.

Protected

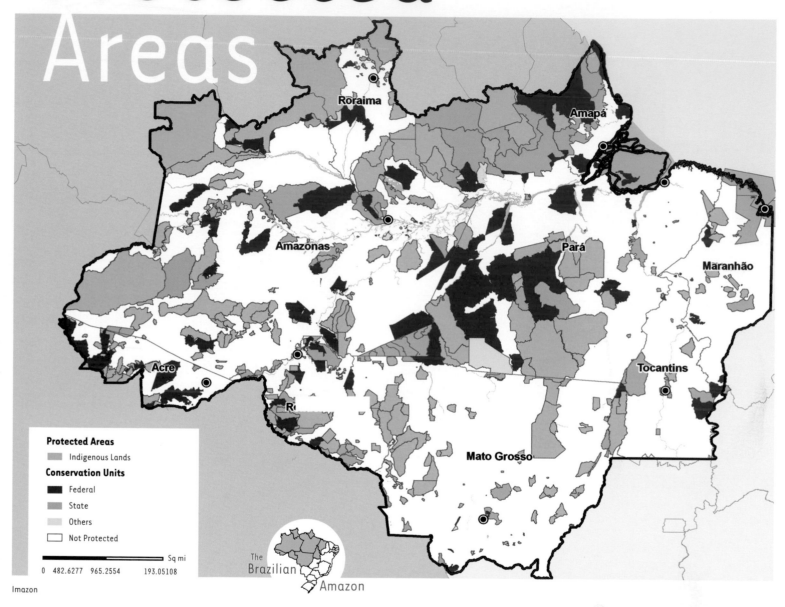

Areas

Protected Areas

| | Indigenous Lands |

Conservation Units

	Federal
	State
	Others
	Not Protected

Sq mi
0   482.6277   965.2554   193.05108

Imazon

The Brazilian Amazon

The protected areas in the Brazilian Amazon include federal, state and municipal conservation units, indigenous lands and community areas.

Most recent conservation units were formed on the borders of deforested areas, thus creating a "green barrier" that restricts unmanageable expansion and preserves traditional communities and ecological corridors.

These protected areas comprise 180 million hectares (36% of the territory) if indigenous lands and areas of sustainable logging management are included.

The number of federal conservation units in Brazil has doubled since 2003 — from 338,000 km^2 / 130,502 sq mi to 534,000 km^2 / 206,178 sq mi in 2007, representing 10% of the Legal Amazon.

Protected areas however are still threatened by invasion of illegal loggers, mining and other illicit activities that generate many conflicts with local residents.

However, the effective consolidation and protection of conservation units still require actions that go beyond paperwork: clear demarcation, surveillance, zoning and development of sustainable activities, such as ecotourism, research and extractivism.

Meeting such requirements will decrease the critical threats posed to many of these areas.

Since 1988, the Brazilian Constitution has granted the traditional peoples of the forest the right to the lands they have traditionally occupied.

Types of Protected Areas

Positive Experiences

Chico Mendes Institute

Promotes the preservation, research and sustainable use of conservation units. Is part of Ministry of the Environment.
www.icmbio.gov.br

The Amazon Region Protected Area (ARPA)

In an effort to safeguard tropical forests, the Brazilian federal government launched the ARPA initiative, in 2002, with the support of WWF Brasil and German institutions. This program currently preserves 119,691 sq mi of environmental reserves and sustainable use areas. Studies on deforestation trends indicate that this program will prevent the emission of 1.8 billion tons of carbon into the atmosphere by 2050.
www.mma.gov.br/port/sca/arpa, www.funbio.org.br

Ecological Corridors

Ecological Corridors are large areas of land, consisting of primary ecosystems managed via the integrative model. They can include federal, state and municipal conservation units, indigenous and private lands.
www.mma.gov.br/corredoresecologicos

National Indians Foundation

www.funai.gov.br

Integral Protection Units

Are vulnerable uninhabited biodiversity reserves. Activities are restricted to ecotourism and scientific research.

Sustainable Use Units

Environmental reserves where traditional communities live, or where economic usage is allowed in accordance with plans for utilization of natural resources, territorial protection and sustainable development.

Indigenous lands

Areas where remaining indigenous populations can protect their ancestral culture and territory.

Communal Lands

Afro-Brazilian ethnic areas (quilombolas) also inhabited by artisenal (traditional) fishermen, babaçu coconut breakers and others.

Trafficking of Animals

11

The largest markets for the illegal trafficking of animals are in the European Community, the Unites States, Japan and China.

Brazil's modern laws concerning environmental crimes are among the most progressive in the world. In recent years inspection efforts have resulted in an increasing number of fines and arrests.

Biopiracy only exists because there are potential buyers.

Approximately 38 millions species of animals are trafficked; only 1 in 10 reaches its destination alive.

The trafficking of wild animals is the third largest illegal business in the world, circulating an estimated 10 billion dollars a year. It is second only to the traffic of arms and drugs.

It has been estimated that over 10% of this amount is generated from wild Amazonian animals.

Arara-azul-de-lear

How much does a dealer pay for a Brazilian macaw in the forest? **U$ 15**
How much does he sell it for in Brazil? **U$ 15,000**
How much does he sell it for in Europe? **U$ 80,000**
Out of every 10 Brazilian macaws captured, how many arrive alive? **Only one.**

Report the illegal trafficking of wild animals!

Positive Experiences

Network Against the Traffic of Wild Animals (RENCTAS)

Develops national campaigns against the trafficking of wild animals and, with the federal government, helps repress organized crime.
www.renctas.org.br

Genetic Heritage Management Council (CGEN)

The council, linked to the Ministry of Environment, is responsible for licensing and monitoring the use of genetic resources and associated traditional knowledge.
www.mma.gov.br/cgen

List against Biopiracy

The Brazilian government has produced a list containing the characteristics of over 3,000 species of flora with the objective of avoiding international brand patent registration and commercial use of their names.
www.inpi.gov.br

Campaign against Biopiracy

In 2003, the "Cupuaçu is Ours" campaign challenged the existence of patents and trademarks on Cupuaçu and products derived from it in Japan, Europe and United States. As a result the "Cupuaçu" trademark was annulled in 2004.
www.amazonlink.org/biopiracy

Anodorhynchus leari

Roads and
Highways
12

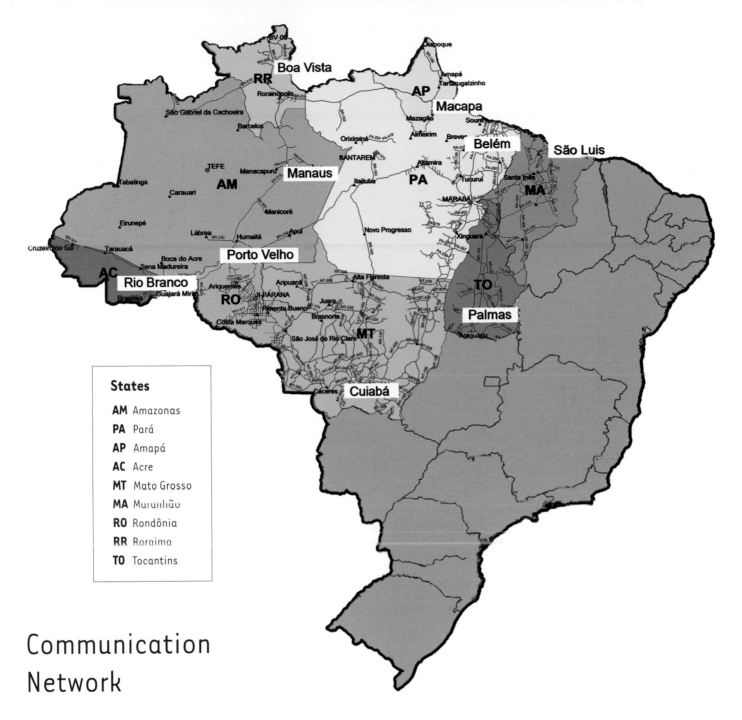

States

AM Amazonas
PA Pará
AP Amapá
AC Acre
MT Mato Grosso
MA Maranhão
RO Rondônia
RR Roraima
TO Tocantins

Communication Network

Historically, the occupation of the Amazon began along its rivers. In the 1970's four major highways were opened to link the Amazon with the Southcentral and Northeast regions of Brazil.

Highways often bring lumber dealers, cattlemen, settlers and new towns.

On the other hand, they also provide isolated populations access to social and economic benefits, as is the case of BR 010 (Belém-Brasília). Once paved, that highway freed the city of Belém from 350 years of isolation.

Roads are certainly necessary; however, if not well planned they can cause irreparable damage to a region.

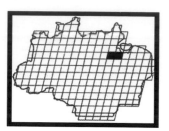

BR 230, Transamazonica Highway / INPE

Fish Bone Effect

Two thirds of the deforestation in the
Amazon takes place along the highways.
Successive developments open new
areas of occupation, creating the
fish bone effect.

Imazon

Clandestine Roads

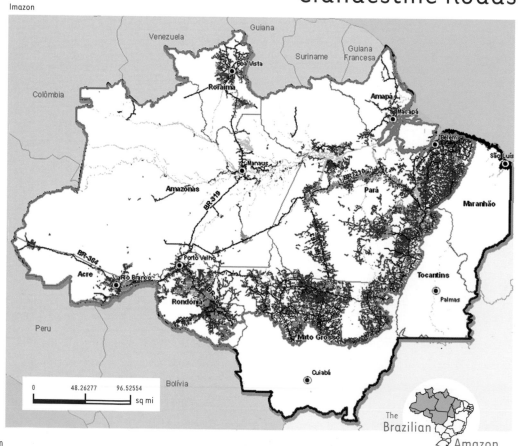

According to recent surveys,
about 173,000 km / 107,497
miles of clandestine roads run
in the heart of the Brazilian
Amazon. The invaders build the
roads under the largest trees
during the wet season, when
the clouds reduce satellite
visibility. Clandestine roads
are also concentrated in the
deforestation arch.

	Amazon Biome
Roads	
▬	Official
▬	Unofficial
▬	On Settlements
⊙	State Capital
▢	Legal Amazon boundaries
▢	State boundaries
▢	States out of Legal Amazon boundaries
▢	International boundaries
▢	Hydrography

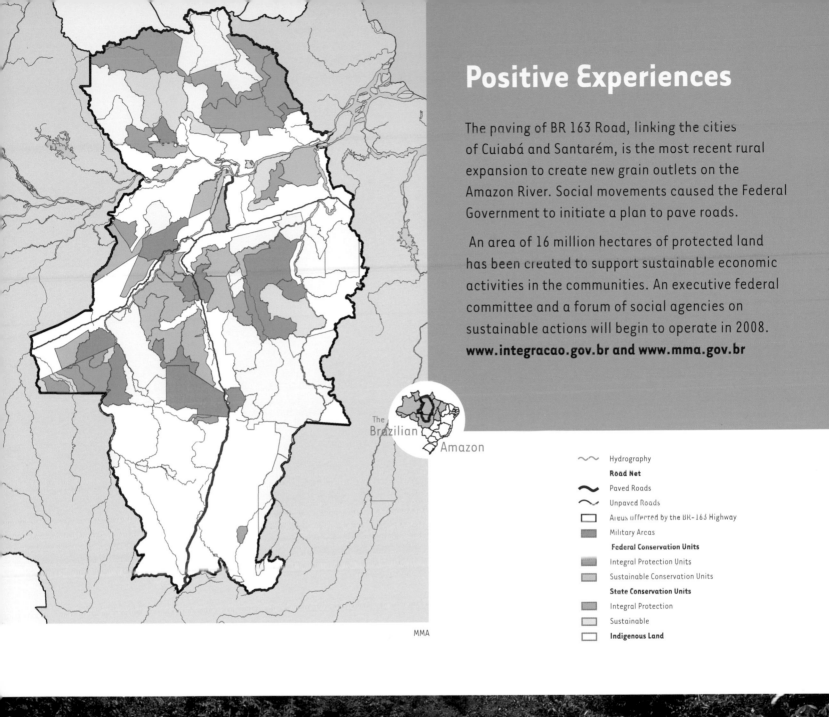

Positive Experiences

The paving of BR 163 Road, linking the cities of Cuiabá and Santarém, is the most recent rural expansion to create new grain outlets on the Amazon River. Social movements caused the Federal Government to initiate a plan to pave roads.

An area of 16 million hectares of protected land has been created to support sustainable economic activities in the communities. An executive federal committee and a forum of social agencies on sustainable actions will begin to operate in 2008. **www.integracao.gov.br and www.mma.gov.br**

The Brazilian Amazon

MMA

∼∼∼	Hydrography
	Road Net
∼∼∼	Paved Roads
∼∼∼	Unpaved Roads
▭	Areas offered by the BR-163 Highway
▪	Military Areas
	Federal Conservation Units
▪	Integral Protection Units
▪	Sustainable Conservation Units
	State Conservation Units
▪	Integral Protection
▪	Sustainable
▭	**Indigenous Land**

Wood
and Lumber

13

Today, the Brazilian Amazon is the biggest tropical wood production center on the planet.

There are over 5,000 tree species in the Amazon forest;

only 350 of which are utilized commercially.

However, less than 30 species account for 80% of the lumber market.

These species, such as mahogany (*Swietenia macrophylla*), are threatened.

Many can only be commercialized with special authorization of CITES

(International Convention for the Traffic of Wild Species).

Lumber Frontiers / 2008

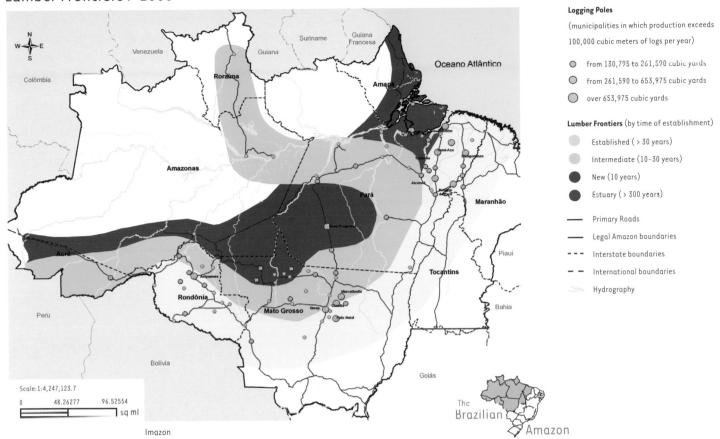

Logging Poles
(municipalities in which production exceeds 100,000 cubic meters of logs per year)

- from 130,795 to 261,590 cubic yards
- from 261,590 to 653,975 cubic yards
- over 653,975 cubic yards

Lumber Frontiers (by time of establishment)

- Established (> 30 years)
- Intermediate (10-30 years)
- New (10 years)
- Estuary (> 300 years)

— Primary Roads
— Legal Amazon boundaries
-- Interstate boundaries
- - International boundaries
⌇ Hydrography

Scale: 1:4,247,123.7

0   48.26277   96.52554
sq ml

Imazon

The Brazilian Amazon

Approximately 10 million trees are removed from the forest every year, 70% are the result of illegal lumbering. Only 30% of lumber extraction is authorized and only 3% of that is certified internationally.

The predatory exploitation of lumber is one of the main threats to the integrity of the forests. There are over 3 thousand mills, many of which are clandestine.

The global demand for wood is enormous, in particular for the valuable tropical hardwood, which only occurs in native forests. Lumber mills are therefore voraciously invading the remaining reserves.

The lower costs of illegal and predatory timber exploitation reduces the competitiveness of certified industries that follow environmental and sustainable guidelines.

Consumer centers in Brazil, Europe, Asia and the US still purchase timber lacking certification!

The Waste Factor

Almost 65% of timber extracted in the predatory process is wasted.

It all begins in the jungle when trees are chosen regardless of any social or environmental criteria.

For each tree harvested for its valuable timber, 20 additional trees of various species are also cut down because of their tangled branches, vines, treetops and roots.

In just a few days, illegal sawmills can be easily installed in the heart of the forest. Loggers know what to do to stay unnoticed.

Lack of training and technology at the sawmills account for 50% of wasted wood.

Some loggers re-use the permits assigned to one lot of trees to explore other areas and counterfeit transportation permits.

Do your part! Only buy wood with an environmental certification!

Sustainable Timber Extraction

If carried out responsibly, timber production can be one of the most important forms of sustainable development.

Correct and responsible methods of timber harvesting protect the integrity of the forest.

Harvest areas are identified, numbered, measured and mapped to minimize soil disturbance. Area rotation technique allows the use of land every 30 years.

Forests near streams and waterways are untouched and protected.

Vines are removed and the appropriate felling techniques - including directional felling - avoid harming neighboring trees.

In order to be harvested, trees must have a specific diameter and be surrounded by other grown trees of the same species. An average of 3 to 5 trees per hectare (107,639 sq ft) are harvested.

Matrix trees are preserved to ensure the germination of seeds of each species.

Roads and skid trails are planned in detail, tree trunks are carefully transported, and waste is minimized at the sawmill.

Naturally fallen trees are also utilized.

Every year, over 700 million trees die in the forest, but not all have commercial value .

In recent years, government and consumer demands have helped increase the number of certified lumber areas in the Amazon.

The Public Forest Management Act, (Bill 11.284/ 2006) regulates the sustainable use and concession of public forests in Brazil (75% of the country's territory). Government and independent auditors are in charge of supervision.

By 2016, 25 million hectares will be set aside for communal use, and an additional 13 million hectares will be reserved for companies with 30 to 60 year contracts.

Sustainable Forest Districts have been created in partnership with institutions providing education, research, renewable energy and social development.

Brazilian Forest Service

www.mma.gov.br/sfb

Positive Experiences

FSC- Brazilian Council of Forestry Handling

A non-governmental organization that promotes forestry handling and certification based on environmental, social and economic criteria. FSC is comprised of environmental institutions, businesses and social movements committed to transparent certification regulations in Brazil and other countries.

www.fsc.org.br | www.fsc.org

Producers

PFCA - Amazon Certified Producers Association

The first Brazilian association that brings together Amazon certified producers and traditional communities involved in forest management based on FSA models.

www.pfca.org.br

Buyers

Organizations that only purchase certified lumber, and are engaged in the expansion of sustainable markets. Joint purchases create better delivery conditions and competitive prices.

www.manejoflorestal.org

Community Lumber

Small associations of local communities involved in projects for the sustainable use of lumber and re-utilization of forest residue. Projects such as these have created subsidies for new policies in the lumber business.

www.ibama.gov.br/promanejo

Cattle Raising

14

Cattle raising accounts for 2/3 of the deforestation in the Amazon, an area the size of California. (470,000 km^2 / 181,468 sq mi)

Low productivity management systems still rely on extensive pastures (0.7 head/hectare).

Almost half of the pastures are abandoned once the soil is depleted.

In the cattle raising industry, an area of 5 thousand hectares employs 10 people; in forestry management, the same size area employs 800 people.

In less than 30 years, the Amazon's cattle herd has increased from 1 million to 70 million head.

Most of beef consumption is domestic, but international demand is increasing.

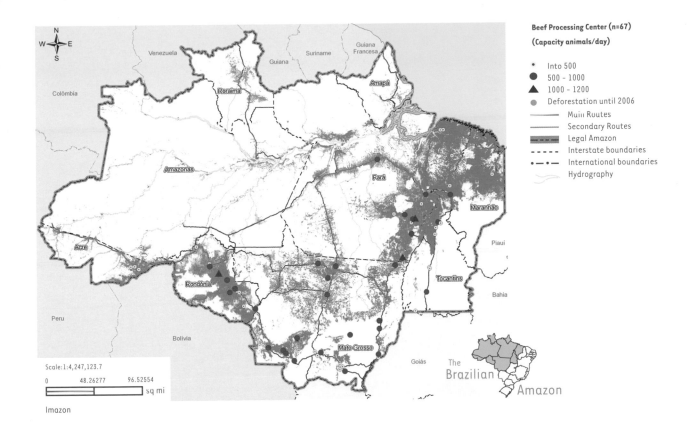

Imazon

Beef Processing Center (n=67)
(Capacity animals/day)

- Into 500
- 500 – 1000
- 1000 – 1200
- Deforestation until 2006
- Main Routes
- Secondary Routes
- Legal Amazon
- Interstate boundaries
- International boundaries
- Hydrography

Scale:1:4,247,123.7

0   48.26277   96.52554

sq mi

The Brazilian Amazon

Sustainable Cattle Raising

Extensive areas previously opened can continue to be used without further deforestation.

New, modern, intensive technologies have helped increase land productivity.

In areas where these technologies are implemented, cattle raising can be highly profitable, as long as policies are respected. These initiatives could double the agricultural lands of Brazil. However, the available technologies are still very expensive.

Some flatland areas of the Amazon, where cattle can graze freely, produce high quality beef with international health certification.

Positive Experiences

Organic Cattle Raising

A number of organizations and initiatives are involved in setting criteria for the sustainable production of cattle, forest management and agriculture. Market expectations are leading to expansion in these areas.
**www.cpafac.embrapa.br | www.wwf.org.br
www.aliancadaterra.org.br**

The Executive Plan for Sustainable Development of Agribusiness in the Amazon

The Brazilian government launched, in 2006, an executive plan to restore the extensive degraded pastureland and monoculture areas in the Legal Amazon.
www.agricultura.gov.br

Soy and Agrobusiness

15

Soy agriculture occupies vast areas of land and
entirely eliminates the nutrient-rich topsoil. The
deforestation that precedes soy implantation
causes severe climate and humidty change and
silting of rivers; additionally the growing of this
crop is a source of agrotoxic contamination.

Soy is now the leading cause of rainforest destruction in the Brazilian Amazon.

The expansion of soybean cultivation in vast mechanized fields generates few jobs.

As a result, small landowners and traditional communities leave their lands, generating rural exodus and subsequent population increase in urban shantytowns. The advancement of soy production in the Amazon also results in concentration of income and rural violence.

Over 90% of the 787 thousand tons of soy exported from the Amazon in 2005 was sent to Europe to be used in the animal feed industry.

In some regions in Amazonia, such as Santarém, there has been a 500% increase of deforested areas due to soy plantation between 2002 and 2006. Pigs and chicken are fed with fallen forests!

Biofuel, while potentially beneficial to the environment, may represent a new pressure to the Amazonian byome.

Positive Experiences

Deforestation Moratorium

Following a number of national and international protests led by Greenpeace International, in June 2006, key businesses have committed to a two-year soy-free Amazon forest moratorium. This initiative has involved the Brazilian Association of Vegetable Oil Industries.
www.greenpeace.org/international/press/reports/ eating-up-the-amazon | www.greenpeace.org.br www.abiove.com.br/

Remote Licensing

Soy producers, farm owners, government officials and NGOs in the depleted state of Mato Grosso have banded together to regulate and apply environmental and social guidelines throughout the state. Satellite monitoring will be used in all land concessions by 2010.
www.nature.org and www.mt.gov.br

Even though soy is important to our everyday modern lives, let's not use the Amazonian biome for its cultivation.

Fire

16

Both small producers and big rural owners use fire to prepare the land for agriculture and cattle raising. It is a quick and economical way to fertilize the soil and to control pests and diseases in plantations. However, the use of fire quickly depletes the soil.

Neighboring forests are also affected by the heat, which runs below the soil of the forest, burning seeds that have been deposited or planted awaiting rain. This is known as a hidden fire.

Tropical forest fires account for 20% of the world's total greenhouse gas emissions — equivalent to the entire automobile fleet on the planet .

Sustainable technologies for new forms of energy might take time; however, eliminating deforestation in tropical areas may cause an immediate and proportional reduction in gas emissions.

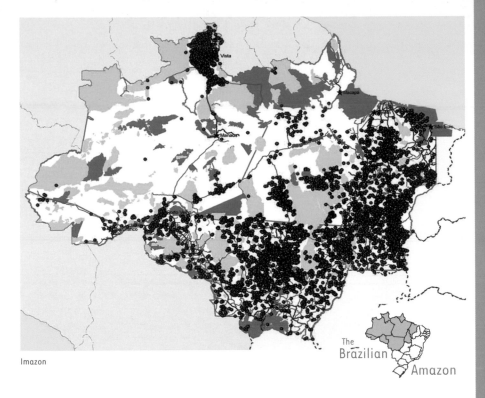

Imazon

Heat Sources in the Brazilian Amazon

In **2004** - 173,236 sources / year
In **2005** - 161,374 sources / year
In **2006** - 117,320 sources / year
In **2007** - 66,911 sources / year

Not all blazes or sources of heat are a fire – in the Amazon, fires have been a traditional land clearing practice. A forest fire is an uncontrolled fire.

The Brazilian Amazon

Solutions

• Implementation of agroforestry systems
• Controlled burning – use of fire when humidity is higher (e.g. dawn or sunset), use of clearings, waiting for rain before setting a second fire, observing wind direction
• Environmental License System in Rural Properties (SLAPR); by locating rural properties via satellite, the system verifies the compliance of deforestation and controlled fires licenses.
• Environmental education – discussion in communities and in the media about the damages caused by fire in agriculture and cattle raising.
• Creation of community fire brigades.

Positive Experiences

Amazon Fire Prevention and Control Project (PROARCO)

PROARCO monitors heat sources in the Amazon, aiming at forest fire prevention in deforested federal areas. It conducts enforcement operations as well as preventive and educational actions during critical periods.
www.ibama.gov.br/proarco/home.htm

Protect Program (Proteger)

Between 1998 and 2006, led by the Working Amazon Group with international support and cooperation, the social movements of the Amazon developed a large mobilization of communities to control the use of fire.
www.proteger.org.br

Tipitamba Project

Since 1995, Project of Northeastern Amazonia promotes mulching equipment, which allows for fire-free land preparation, providing an alternative to slash-and-burn.
www.cpatu.embrapa.br

Commercial Fishing 17

Commercial fishing employs over 100 thousand people and generates approximately U$ 120 million/year, for a total catch of 80 thousand tons (roughly 50% of Brazil's production of freshwater fish).

The use of large nets — up to 1 km / 0.62 mile — are a threat to fish species and reduce the fish stock consumed by the riverside communities.

Recent research has demonstrated the viability of regulating and protecting fish stock in the region.

Efforts in fishing prohibition during reproductive periods, management of lakes, fishing agreements and subsistence fisheries are all paying off; these practices have avoided the extinction of many species and have increased the offer of sustainable produced fish.

However, in order to effectively curb the threat of depletion these regulatory practices need to be implemented on a much larger scale.

Positive Experiences

ProVárzea (Lowland Natural Resources Handling Project)

With international cooperation, it studies the conservation of fishing resources and supports local inhabitants' initiatives, through municipal agreements pertaining to fishing and lake conservation by local communities.
www.ibama.gov.br/provarzea

Yikatu Xingu

Campaign inspired by leaders at the Xingu National Park, created in 2004 to find solutions to protect and restore the river sources bringing together rural producers, indigenous people, researchers and civil society organizations.
www.yikatuxingu.org.br

Aquatic Biodiversity Project

www.mma.gov.br/aquabio

Predatory fishing practices target only a few species: pirarucu (*Arapaima gigas*), tambaqui (*Colossoma macropomum*), tucunaré (*Cichla* spp), surubim (*Pimelodidae* spp) but end up wasting large numbers of less valued fish.

18
Predatory Economy

The period of "boom", fuelled by predatory development that generates immediate profits, quickly gives way to economic and social decline in many regions ("bust").

Cities and the highest violence rates in Brazil / Arch of Deforestation

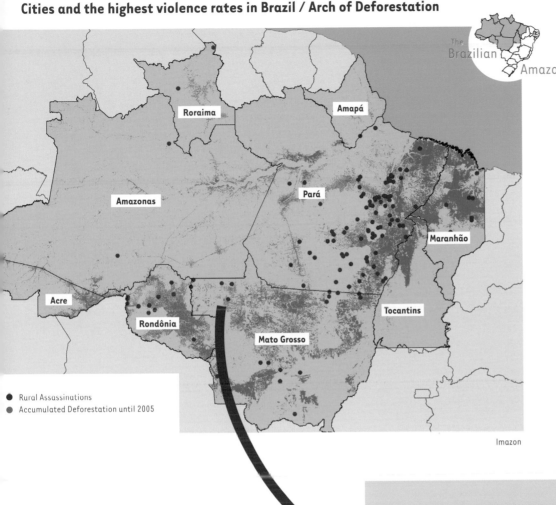

The
Brazilian
Amazon

- ● Rural Assassinations
- ● Accumulated Deforestation until 2005

Imazon

Deforestation and Violence

In the Brazilian Amazon, 61% of the municipalities that register the highest deforestation rates also register the highest homicide rates.

Illegal land grabs have become one of the most powerful means of land-based domination in the Amazon resulting in major social disparities and violence against traditional and indigenous communities.

Deforested areas are abandoned and the land is transformed into nutrient-poor pasture or farmland. Development of deforested areas has so far not significantly improved the economic welfare of the local population.

The case of Colniza

Colniza, located 723 miles northeast of Cuiabá, the capital of the state of Mato Grosso, occupies a large portion of a 2.8 million hectare protected area. However, in 2003 of all Amazon municipalities, it ranked fourth in deforestation, and reported the highest annual homicide rate in the country (165 for every 100,000 inhabitants).

In September 2004 alone, 19 thousand hectares of forest were destroyed. A number of conflicts in indigenous lands were identified: survivors have said they witnessed massacres of entire groups of indigenous people. In recent years, the government and the army began to take action to recover social and environmental order in the region.

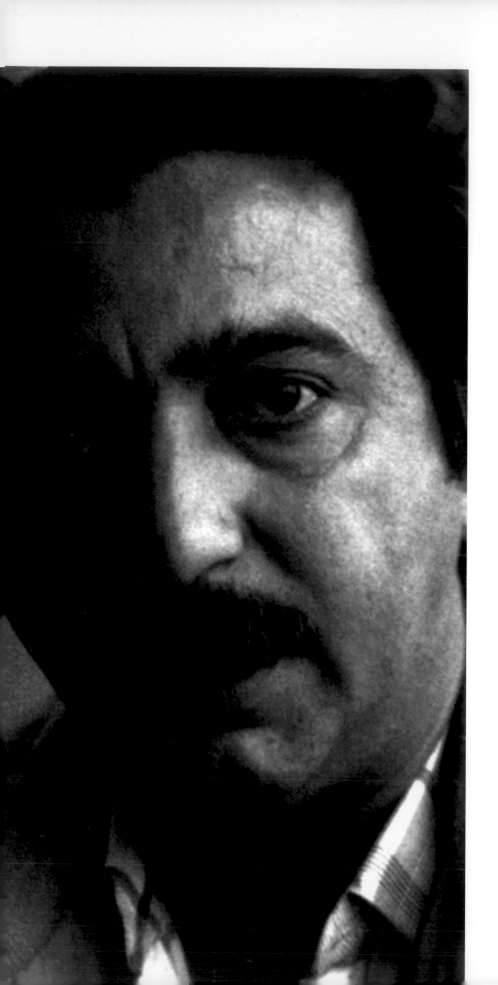

2008: 20 years of Chico Mendes's death

"The Amazon is occupied.
In every corner there are Indians, people working, extracting rubber, and at the same time, fighting for the conservation of nature. As long as Indians and rubber tappers are still in the Amazon jungles, there is hope that it may be saved. We want to create a policy that protects the future of the workers that have lived in Amazonia for centuries and at the same time keep it productive.
I believe that each one of us has the important mission to commit to the protection of this region and its peoples. This is not a struggle of the workers only; it is a struggle of the Brazilian society as a whole."

Chico Mendes, assassinated in the State of Acre, in 1988

Every year, hundreds of leaders are killed

defending their communities and natural resources. These communities and their leaders have few resources and are under tremendous economic pressure; yet they dedicate their daily lives to protect the forests, its culture and a balanced life style with nature.

This is a hidden battle. Often crimes are badly documented, legal processes are long and require a lot of resources. And, unfortunately, the level of impunity is still astonishingly high.

Chico Mendes was a historical leader of the rubber extractors. Working in the south of Acre, in the 70's and 80's, together with his companions, he developed a non-violent technique to prevent trees from being felled by large scale ranchers known as empate or stalemate: At a prearranged time, the rubber tappers - sometimes with their families, surrounded the lumberjacks, blocked roads, and called the public's attention to this organized destruction of the forests.

Where traditional population exists, the forest is preserved.

Chico Mendes and his companions created a new model of united conservation - the Extractive Reserve - where the Federal Government owns the area, but local communities explore its natural resources, obeying a community plan.

Dorothy Stang

Sister Dorothy Stang, a North American naturalized Brazilian missionary, was murdered in 2005, in the town of Anapu, in the state of Pará. She was 72 years old.

Many killings over land disputes occur in the region and very few result in convictions.

However, Dorothy Stang's murderers were convicted which has created new hopes for a more rigorous law enforcement that will bring criminals to justice.

"The death of the forest is the end of our lives"

(Dorothy Stang, assassinated in 2005)

Positive Experiences

Attorney General

Federal attorneys in Brazil are leading the process of reclaiming millions of hectares of public land that have been illegally occupied. Over 15 million hectares have been reclaimed since 2000. **www.pgr.mpf.gov.br**

Ministry of Labor

Maintains repression teams to control slave or semi-slave labor, and enforces rural and urban workers rights in deforested areas. The International Labor Organization estimates that 30.000 workers are held in slavery in Brazil. **www.trabalho.gov.br/trab_escravo**

Social Cartography Project

Creates maps based on the perspective of the traditional indigenous and rural peoples in Amazonia, and maps of social conflicts in forests and urban regions. Anthropologist Alfredo Wagner de Almeida devised the project, with the support of the Ford Foundation. **www.ufam.edu.br**

Pastoral Commission for Land

Offers community support, campaigning for social justice and observance of human rights for small farmers and the landless; produces annual report on land-inspired human rights violations and conflicts. **www.cptnac.org.br**

Other links

National Confederation of Rural Workers

A network of family and paid rural workers unions; leads an extensive mass mobilization process, such as Gritos da Terra (The Cries of the Land). **www.contag.org.br**

MST - Movement of Landless Workers

Organization that promotes land reform on the borders of deforested regions. **www.mst.org.br**

19

Great Projects

Growth Acceleration Program

The Brazilian Growth Acceleration Program (PAC) plans to invest billions of reais in the social sector, housing, scientific research and sanitation, as well as in the infrastructure, such as roads, railroads, gas ducts and hydroelectric plants. However, the social and environmental impacts of program are still a cause for concern. Additionally, in South America, there are also projects underway to construct a transoceanic highway that will bridge the Pacific and Atlantic oceans.

www.presidencia.gov.br
www.iirsa.org
www.iadb.org
www.biceca.org
http://science.conservation.org/portal/server.pt

The Brazilian Growth Acceleration Program (PAC) - Energy, transportation and protected areas

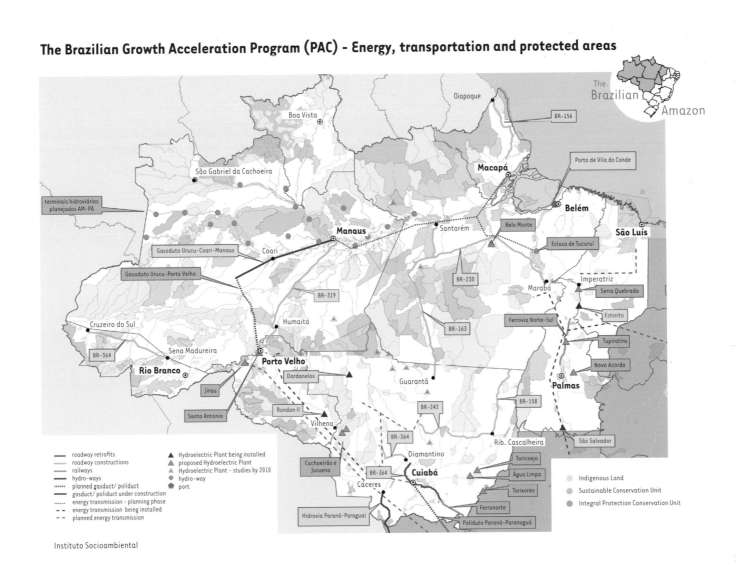

Instituto Socioambiental

Geodiversity and Mining

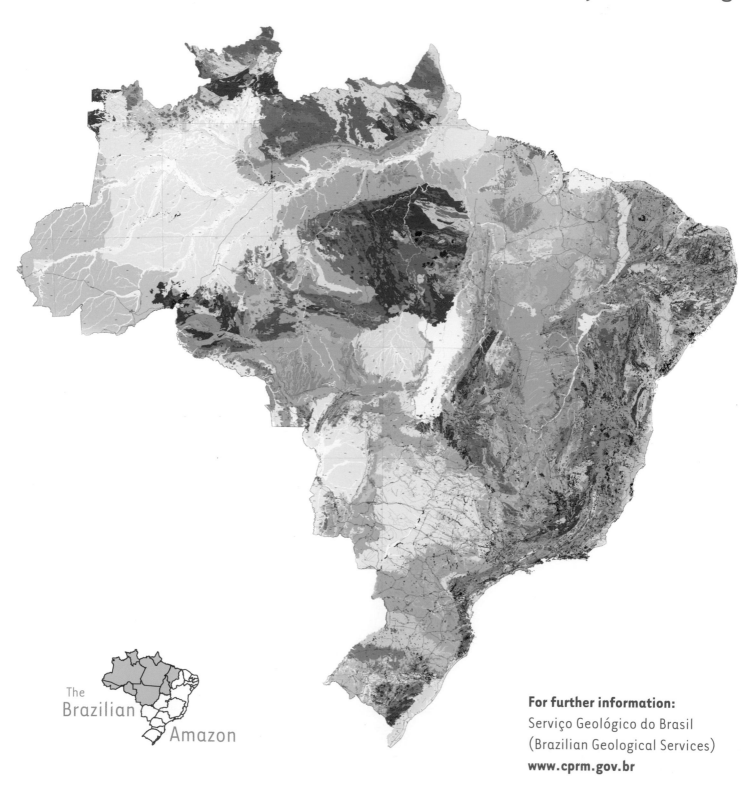

The
Brazilian
Amazon

For further information:
Serviço Geológico do Brasil
(Brazilian Geological Services)
www.cprm.gov.br

The Brazilian Amazon hosts one of the planet's greatest geological diversities. It has the largest iron mine and is ranked third in global bauxite reserves. Mineral reserves include manganese, copper, pewter, nickel, kaolin, potassium, tungsten, titanium, limestone, zinc, unrefined salt, niobium, molybdenum and natural gas.

Historically companies extracting these minerals have only cared about removing the minerals as cheaply and quickly as possible. This has resulted in major conflicts in the region. It has caused large-scale environmental damages to the land as well as economic losses to the local populations, who receive few of the profits from the mining operation and are left to live in the ravaged areas. Secondary businesses and steel plants use wood from deforestation to make charcoal. It has been reported that this has been one of the major causes of deforestation in the region.

The activity of mining need not be destructive and uses far less area than, for example, a cattle operation or soybean production. What is needed for mining to become a part of the region's efforts to be sustainable are the regular use of environmental impact studies, a close and ongoing involvement with local municipalities and communities, and a willingness to provide support and training aimed at local development. Brazilian law now requires a company to compensate for its environmental impact and to be socially responsible.

Gold Mining Camps

Currently, gold and diamond prospecting in Amazonia causes severe environmental degradation, community conflicts and indigenous land grabbing. Economic and social decadence brings child prostitution, drug consumption and urban violence. Rivers are poisoned with large deposits of oil, heavy metal (mercury used in gold mines) and human waste.

Solutions

- Clean technologies to reduce social and environmental impact.
- Increased social participation in public policies.
- Supervision to ensure observance of the law in all operations.
- Social and basic welfare for legal miners.
- Commercial control of smuggling.
- Eviction of invaders from protected areas.
- Greater social participation in the drafting of public policy.
- Involvement of the communities directly affected.

Hydroelectric Power Plants

Amazonia has the world's greatest hydro energy resources. It holds an estimated capacity of 132 thousand MW, the Tocantins basin included.

Although, from the standpoint of carbon emissions, reservoirs are a clean energy alternative, historically they have been constructed at a huge environmental and social cost to native areas, resulting in major conflicts in the region. Brazil's energy demands, according to official estimates, require the generation of 43 thousand MW in the next ten years from the Madeira, Tapajós, Xingu and Tocantins rivers.

The deleterious effects of building a dam are now well-established and call for rigorous pre-assessments, as well as environmental and technical actions that will mitigate the social and economic impact on affected populations.

Execution:

National Agency of Electrical Energy
www.aneel.gov.br

Empresa de Pesquisa Energética
www.epe.gov.br

Critics:

World Dams Comission
www.dams.org

Live Rio Madeira Campaign
www.madeiravivo.org.br

Live Xingu Campaign
http://xinguvivo.blogspot.com

Movement of Dam
Affected People
www.mabnacional.org.br

Alternative sources of energy that can be implemented in Amazonia include solar energy, small-scale hydro plants, underwater-turbines and biodiesel produced with native species such as andiroba and babaçu palms. However, these initiatives still operate on a very local and experimental basis.

Aruan waterfall

Juruti: A 21st Century Initiative

Alcoa is laying down the foundations of a world-class, innovative bauxite mining operation in the municipality of Juruti, in the heart of the Brazilian Amazon, conceived and operated according to 21st century social, environmental and economic standards.

From its inception in 2005, the Juruti project aimed at setting a new standard, establishing a clear and close connection with the local community, exceeding all legal Brazilian requirements and promoting sustainable environmental practices throughout the region.

Over 7,000 citizens, as part of the licensing process, participated in public hearings held in Juruti, Santarém and Belém - the latter the capital of the State of Pará - generating widespread popular support for its implementation. The physical layout of the project - comprising a port on the Amazon River, a railroad and a mining - crushing-washing complex - has no walls to separate the community from the operation, in contrast to traditional mining operations in Brazil and around the world. Pointedly, there is also no area specifically set aside for a mine management housing compound - full integration with the community is a consequence. Significant efforts were expended prior to construction to assure preservation of archeological artifacts and local flora and fauna. World-class environmental and engineering know-how was brought into play to assure that the permanent environmental footprint of the project was as small as possible - in fact, it is one-half of the licensed area. Careful attention has been paid to the vast forest areas surrounding the project, where, Alcoa, in conjunction with a NGO (Non-Governmental Organization), developed a multi-year program aimed at preserving the biodiversity of that region. And importantly, from inception, the thrust of the Juruti project has been to assure the sustainable development of the region, to allow for the continued welfare of the population after the exhaustion of the bauxite reserves, currently estimated at over fifty years; accordingly a series of initiatives are underway to build sustainable activities in the region.

Other key dimensions of the Juruti project encompass the emphasis placed on employing talent from Juruti and the State of Pará from construction to operation, a local supplier program to ensure the building of capabilities and entrepreneurship in the region, initiatives aimed at preserving and fostering the local culture and traditions and the partnering with local government institutions and a multitude of Brazilian and international NGO's in the field of social and environmental development.

Founded in 1888, Alcoa is the leader in the global aluminum industry and has been a successful corporate citizen in Brazil for over forty years. Alcoa has been successively recognized in global forums as a leader in translating Sustainability concepts into effective practice - the Juruti bauxite mine in the heartland of the Amazon is proud to be an integral part of this tradition.

www.alcoa.com.br/juruti

Positive Experiences

Sustainable Amazon Plan

Brazil's regional development plan for Amazonia is the work of 11 ministries and involves the cooperation of the federal, state and municipal governments, the parliament, civil society and private initiatives. The plan addresses infrastructure, territorial management, sustainable production, new financing plans, and social participation by citizens. The plan was launched in 2003,and, in spite of initial setbacks, major policies that make sustainability a top priority are currently being established.

www.integracao.gov.br www.mma.gov.br | www.simposioamazonia.com.br

Ecological and Economic Zoning Plan

The Ecological and Economic Zoning Plan (ZEE) focuses on determining the best land use of each area of the Amazon, based on its specific conditions and environmental characteristics. The territorial planning, or ecosystem management process, uses a scale of 1/1 million. However, operational indicators require a 1/250 million scale. Once approved by state commissions, the ZEE will be implemented in 2008 as a mechanism to restrain the expansion of land used for producing sugar cane (ethanol) and biodiesel in the region.

www.mma.gov.br/estruturas/PZEE/_arquivos/index.html

The Pilot Program for the Protection of Brazil's Tropical Forests (PPG7)

This major international cooperation initiative in the Brazilian Amazon partners with the World Bank, the European Union, USAID and other agencies. With the active participation of NGOs and other social movements, this program promotes and develops hundreds of projects related to the social wellbeing of local populations, scientific research and income generation.

www.mma.gov.br/port/sca/ppg7/index.html | www.rfpp.org

Light for Everyone

A national program developed by the Ministry of Energy for the inclusion of energy services, benefiting 12 million people. It prioritizes rural areas with low Human Development rates. In the Amazon, the program includes local initiatives for developing sustainable sources of solar energy.

www.mme.gov.br

Cities
and Urbanization

Today, 17 million people —
2/3 of the Brazilian Amazon
population — live in areas
considered to be urban.
The population density of
the Brazilian Amazon is 4.5
inhabitants/km2, but the human
distribution is quite irregular.

20

City of Tefé on the Solimões River

The urbanization rates have increased from 30% in 1970 to 70% in 2004, which includes migration waves from other parts of Brazil. Whereas the average rural urbanization rate was 43%, some urban areas showed an increase of 274%, indicating forest migration to the cities.

Population in Legal Amazonia *in thousand of inhabitants	1950	1960	1970	1980	1990	2000	2005
	3,820	5,647	7,717	11,757	16,988	21,052	23,606

Most of the 768 cities are small towns located in deforested areas.

Larger cities, such as Belém and Manaus, rapidly developed during the rubber boom in the 19th century. Today, each city is home to pproximately 2 million people. The zona franca's (free trade zone) industrial facilities produce high-tech electronics with little environmental impact.

São Sebastião Square
Manaus Industrial District
The Port of Manaus

In 2007, the poverty rate in urban Amazonia was estimated at 45%. Treated water was available to only 68% of the population and the sewage system to only 48%.

For the most part, cities in the Amazon are beautiful with old and ornate architecture, and are located on the region's riverbanks and beaches.

These cities face the same problems as other large urban centers in poor and developing countries: population growth, deficient infrastructure, poor access to public services, high rates of menial jobs, unemployment and an informal economy.

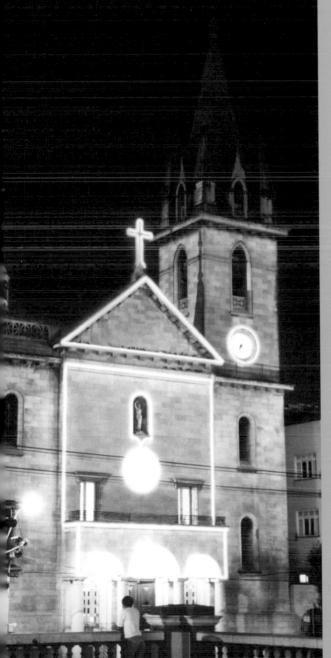

Positive Experiences

The Local Agenda 21

A local government-led effort seeking to avoid
inordinate urban growth by involving the entire
community in action strategies aimed at the
sustainable development of the region.
www.mma.gov.br/agenda21

Participatory Management Plans

The Ministry of Cities is responsible for developing
and managing an urban development policy in cities
with over 20 thousand inhabitants. It also instructs
local governments in matters related to planning and
territorial management.
www.cidades.gov.br

Cities' Friends of the Amazon

The program seeks to elicit commitments from
municipal governments to exclusively use timber
of legal origin, among other initiatives.
www.greenpeace.org.br/cidadesamigas

21

Global Consumption

The destruction of Amazonia has historic roots. All nations, directly or indirectly, contribute to the destruction as they give in to the pressures of uncontrolled consumerism and predatory economic development at any cost.

For example, it is estimated that in the 1990s at least half of the ground newly put to agricultural use was previously natural forest.

This is part of a global phenomenon

in which everyone should be held accountable. Industrialization has resulted in the use of pollutant fuels, energy waste, abusive consumerism and the voracious destruction of green areas in search of raw materials.

Ecological Footprint of Nations

Analyses of current human consumption habits and their impact on the planet may indicate a need for human society to move in entirely new directions.

"If other countries fail to do anything, the planet's temperature will continue to rise and Amazonia will be destroyed anyway."

Carlos Nobre

Balance Natural Resources /Consumption

Mongolia	+ 137,95
Namibia	+ 94,11
Papua Nova Guine	+ 50,28
New Zealand	+ 33,72
Uruguay	+ 17,19
Brazil	+ 10, 38
Costa Rica	+ 3,96
India	+ 2,20
Canada	- 0,21
China	- 3,77
Russia	- 13,11
Finland	- 14,45
United States	- 83,60
United Arab Emirates	- 199,66

Adapted from Redefining Progress, 2005

www.ecologicalfootprint.org/pdf/
Footprint%20of%20Nations%202005.pdf

Amazonia [22]
and Global Climate

"Amazonia is a critical
area when assessing
any matter related to
the future of the Earth,
humankind and of
this country where we live"

Luis Emgydio de Mello Filho

Hadley Circuit

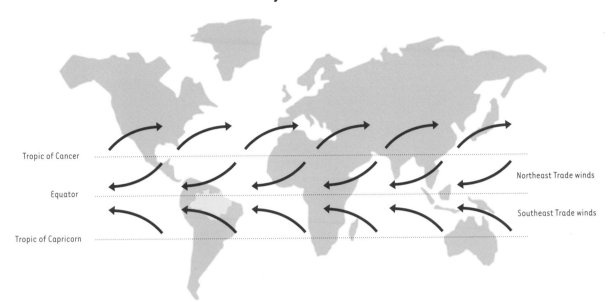

Tropic of Cancer

Equator

Tropic of Capricorn

Northeast Trade winds

Southeast Trade winds

Amazonia, with its vast forests, is one of the world's climate regulators.

A Gigantic Air Conditioning System

How flying rivers are formed

Every day the forest releases into the atmosphere a volume of water equivalent to another Amazon River!

The Amazon region is a huge water vapor generator, not only essential to cloud formation, but also a determinant of regional and even planetary climate.

Every day, the forest releases billions of liters of water into the air and when this humid mass of air meets the Andes Mountain Range, it is forced southwards, forming airborne rivers known as the flying rivers.

These flying rivers influence the climate of the rest of the continent. They benefit the climate and economic development of vast regions of South America that otherwise would be deserts.

During the natural process of humidity and temperature regulation, the forest supplies water vapor to the clouds. Clouds then return the water to the forest, cooling the air like a huge air conditioner. Ongoing forest processes such as organic decay and plant transpiration produce 60% of the rain during this cycle.

Volatile organic compounds (VOCs) are microscopic particles that play an important role in this cycle. Because VOCs emit gases we encounter them in the forest through our noses-the fresh scent of a tree, the sweet bouquet of a flower, or the sharp odor an animal gives off warning you not to attack.

In the forest there are immense quantities of VOCs. The water vapor in the forest attaches to these particles; the water vapor condenses, creating low clouds and heavy rainfall.

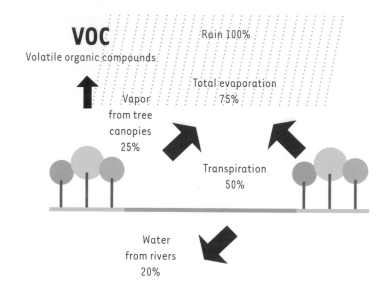

VOC
Volatile organic compounds

Rain 100%

Total evaporation 75%

Vapor from tree canopies 25%

Transpiration 50%

Water from rivers 20%

The destruction of Amazonia can change our planet's climate.

6% of the planet's gas emission

Smoke from slash and burning in Southeastern Amazonia

The Carbon Balance

Through photosynthesis, the forest captures CO_2 from the atmosphere and incorporates it into its biomass – trunks, branches and roots. This process, known as carbon sequestration, can result in fewer greenhouse emissions being released into the atmosphere.

Climate studies of Amazonia have demonstrated that the current forest sequesters more carbon from the atmosphere than it releases, confirming the belief that a live forest provides a huge environmental service.

The carbon stock in Amazonia is estimated to account for 30% of carbon stored globally.

When a forest is burned, thousands of tons of carbon stored in the biomass are abruptly released into the atmosphere. The replacement of the forest with pastureland means there is relatively little biomass available to recapture or sequester the carbon. Deforestation in the Brazilian Amazon accounts for approximately 6% of the planet's gas emission.

Between 2004 and 2007 Brazil has reduced carbon gas emissions in Amazonia by 500 million tons. This amounts to a 59% reduction of these gases when compared to prior years.

Interrupting this cycle can affect the entire global climate system.

"A forest is a library with books whose value resides not in the information of their pages but, rather, in the carbon they store."

Antonio Nobre

Amazonia and the threats of global warming

Temperature increase may affect rainfall. Additionally, as the temperature rises and removes moisture from the forest, the risk of fires may increase and further the chain of destruction.

Regardless of what global warming scenarios unfold, an increase in ocean water levels and changes in the oceanic currents can cause abrupt changes in Amazonia, which is one of the world's most sensitive biomes.

Future generations will evaluate our responses to climate changes as a measure of our ethical values.

(Human Development Report, 2007/2008, PNUD)

Positive Experiences

LBA - Large Scale Biosphere Atmosphere Project in the Amazon

This international research initiative, led by Brazil in partnership with NASA and other agencies, studies the interaction between the Amazon forest and atmospheric conditions on a regional and global scale. The results of these studies provide scientific support for the sustainable use of natural resources.

http://lba.inpa.gov.br/lba/

The Flying Rivers Project

An initiative of the Brasil das Águas project, this program analyzes and interprets samples of "airborne rivers" that transport water from the Amazon to the Pratu Basin. Hydroplanes collect water vapor and water samples from this region that covers an area of thousands of miles.

www.riosvoadores.com.br

Proambiente - Socio-environmental Program for Rural Family Production

Created in 2002 by social and environmental movements in Amazonia, and later incorporated as a government pilot project, this program benefits thousands of families involved in sustainable production and in a participatory use of land. This innovative plan provides funds to large-scale environmental services, including those dealing with deforestation and carbon emission reduction through sequestration.

www.mma.gov.br/proambiente

Fund for Protection and Conservation of the Brazilian Amazon

Created by the government of Brazil to reduce deforestation by paying for non-emission of carbon. An independent commission determines how much carbon release has been avoided. Current payment is $5 per ton of avoided carbon emission with the assumption that each hectare of forest sequesters 100 tons of carbon.

www.mma.gov.br, www.bndes.gov.br
www.forumclima.org.br

The Forest Conservation Grant

The Amazonas State Program established this grant so traditional and indigenous populations can be compensated for their role in the conservation of the forests. The State Act for Climate Change has been innovative in the country. The Foundation for a Sustainable Amazon has been recently created to manage the process by offering market shares that will preserve 17 million hectares of state owned lands.

www.sds.am.gov.br

Biocarbon Fund

The World Bank and Global Environmental Fund are investing in pilot projects aimed at conserving tropical forests by compensating Brazil and other countries for reducing the rate of deforestation. Compensation takes the form of subsidies for tourism, forest management and the use of genetic resources.

www.carbonfinance.org

23

A Future for Amazonia

"It is about saving,
while there is still time,
a unique source of life, that,
flourishing tomorrow, will make
the Amazon the big earthly
garden that future mankind
will want to see, smell, feel,
and admire."

Darcy Ribeiro

There is more value to a living forest than a dead one

A living forest has huge economic and scientific potential, which future research and development efforts will help to further realize. There are many alternatives to the recent past's predatory actions that can bring modern development and economic benefits to the peoples in the forest. But it is key to Amazonia's future that the indigenous peoples' ancestral knowledge, including their knowledge of plants and their ecologically sound harvesting techniques, be preserved.

New investment opportunities arise from finding new fibers, oils, wood, fruit, and animals as well as from finding a new use for already discovered flora and fauna. Making use of newly acquired genetic information and of traditional knowledge offer still other opportunities for economic development. But all these pursuits must be undertaken with a commitment to conserving the delicate Amazonian biome.

Primary forests are irreplaceable and a large portion of the native flora and fauna, once lost, are impossible to recoup. Avoiding further deforestation is, therefore, the best option when seeking to mitigate the impact of climate change.

Amazonia has huge economic and scientific potential, yet to be discovered and studied.

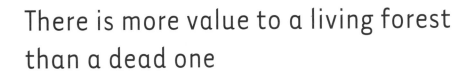

new fibers | oils | wood | fruit | animals | medicinal herbs

Agroforestry

Agroforestry is inspired by the natural forest cycle. Different crops are cultivated at specific times on a plot of land that also hosts native fruit, tropical hardwood and other trees. When the soil eventually loses the nutrients needed to grow the annual crops, trees provide the necessary shade and organic matter to recover the land. Agroforestry eliminates slash and burn methods and doesn't negatively affect the climate.

Natural remedies

Amazonia is a huge natural pharmacy. There are over 1,300 known medicinal plants, and many others are yet to be discovered. Abuses by bio-industries that obtain traditional forest people's recipes, knowledge and even genetic material without prior consent are a common kind of biopiracy.
There are now initiatives in place working to ensure a fair and equitable sharing of benefits from the sustainable use of biological resources.

A Better Future

Territorial occupation policies, ensuring proper use for each specific area of Amazonia.
Law enforcement of land reform regulatory policies.
Effective monitoring and inspections.
Support traditional peoples and respect their lifestyle and knowledge.
Increased scientific research.
Support and extend existing positive projects.
Sustainable economic alternatives.
Forest management, ecotourism, and agro-ecology.
Fair and equitable biodiversity treaties.
Ethical and sustainable partnerships between businesses and local suppliers.
Use of cutting edge technologies for sustainable development.

Conscientious Consumption

Ethics and social responsibility are fundamental to securing our future.

Positive Experiences

Sustainable Amazonia Forum

In 2007, dialogues on cooperation guided by social and environmental responsibility brought together NGOs, civil society organizations, and private companies. A growing number of local, national and international companies are beginning to add sustainability indicators to their agendas.
www.ethos.org.br
www.forumamazoniasustentavel.blogspot.com

Amazon Forever

Led by Brazilian artists, the people in this movement are circulating a petition that demands that deforestation in Amazonia be stopped immediately. The petition also calls for a rigorous implementation of Constitutional laws that institute the Amazon forest as a national treasure. Additionally, the petition invites the entire Brazilian population to put pressure on the government to end the devastation that is now taking place.
www.amazoniaparasempre.com.br

Pact to End Deforestation

The pact is helping to end deforestation through the adoption of a system of reduction targets. The pact provides economic incentives, mainly payment for environmental services.
The campaign, launched by NGO's with the support of governmental agencies, targets 2015 as the year when Brazil will have zero deforestation.
www.ipam.org.br | www.socioambiental.org.br
www.greenpeace.org.br | www.imazon.org.br
www.wwf.org.br | www.conservation.org.br
www.nature.org | www.amazonia.org.br

"We cannot understand life entirely

until we understand the tropical forests."

Norman Myers

Spirits of the Forests

24

Photos: Rodrigo Petrella

Madijá boy

Interacting with the environment

"We learn from childhood that water has its own spirit, rock has its own spirit, the tree another and the same with birds ...we also learn to ask permission of the spirits before we do anything. When we gather material for our crafts or when we cut trees to build our houses, we talk to the spirits and ask for their permission".

Lucas Xunu Meri Guarani

Asheninca people

Spirit of Nature

"The voice of the spirit of nature comes into our minds and tells us about climate changes that are upsetting the way it has always been... what are these times we live in? We are told that the world can come to an end. In order to avoid this, humans must stop, think, and talk to the spirit. A child in the city doesn't know where food comes from. In truth, people that live in the forest spend a lot of time in rituals and live their life in gratitude. When we don't respect the sacred home, or the sacred rock, we cease to respect the spirit."

José Barreto Poani Tuyuka

Nambikwara Shaman

Kuikuro warrior

We need to look after the earth

"Nature is a great mother, no doubt about that. We, Indians, protect nature. The earth, just as any mother, will never complain that her children are wrong, never. So, it is up to us, her children, to protect her, speak to her and look after her. What will happen the day we destroy the earth? Either destruction or fire... the elders have already told us about what has happened in the past; not like you who find out about these things by doing research. These are very ancient stories. We are of another generation. The elders have told us their stories, you understand? They say we need to look after the earth."

Maria Miquelina Machado Tukano

Chief Erikbatsa

The importance of the dream

"Some of our dreams come when our eyes are wide open; we all dream about and envision what we want, about what is really good for us. Other types of dreams come during our sleep. These are the dreams that show us what is good for us, personally, and what is good for our spiritual development. We learn how to interpret dreams in our rituals because they show us our personal and common needs. This is something we learn throughout life; this is how we learn to interact with nature. In the late 80's, medicine men such as Davi Yanomami told us about their dreams, about how progress and great projects could bring great risks to the forest. These aren't mere dreams; these are messages from the spirits. Rituals and festivities are our way to strengthen our connection with the spirits".

Paulo Cipassé Xavante

Mamaende girls

The forest cries

"Humanity is separated by many religions that don't help us find our paths. But nature herself is the strongest possible spirituality. Every time a white man cuts down large trees, the forest cries...he doesn't see how nature reveals her powers when she responds to what is being done to her. Our people use sacred plants to speak with nature and to feel the power of thunder and lightning. We can't imagine what might come if this attitude against nature persists to the extreme".

Paulo Luiz Yawanawá

Kulina woman

Speaking with plants

"The only way we can survive is by not losing the ability to understand the language of the plants, the language of the water, the language of the rock, the language of the winds. Some plants are part of our family... a plant becomes our sister when she lends us her healing sap. And then there are the singing spirits we respect in the parrots".

Kanatyo Pataxó

Amazonia's Stewards: the Peoples of the Forest

25

Over 3 million people live in extractive
and indigenous communities, living
basically on subsistence agriculture
and sustainable harvesting.
With their ancestral wisdom, the
indigenous peoples of the forest
represent the largest peaceful
occupation of the region.
The people in the local communities
protect their environment, their
traditional lifestyle and their
territories, sometimes at the cost
of their own lives; their survival,
after all, depends on the forest.

Amazônia still contains both pre-Colombian concentrations of indigenous crop plant genetic diversity, the major component of agrobiodiversity of interest to indigenous and traditional Amazonian societies, and clear evidence of indigenous technologies used to manage the local environment and its biodiversity.

Thousand of years ago... the beginning of human occupation.

Archeological fragments and artifacts have been found throughout many regions of the Amazon. In addition, "dark earth" found at these archeological sites is highly fertile and suggests deliberate soil improvement techniques were used by ancient civilizations. This evidence dates back 14 thousand years and it suggests that humans inhabited the Americas much earlier than imagined.

Traditional Knowledge

Medicinal herbs and the vast traditional knowledge of forest remedies are a major (and often the sole) resource for people who live in the interior regions of the Amazon. The Ver-o-Peso, in Belém, is the most popular traditional market in the Amazon. Here herb vendors familiar with the traditional medicine of the forest congregate, and it is here that a good part of the fresh produce and medicinal herbs from the region are sold daily.

Pictographs in the Pedra Pintada Cavern, in Monte Alegre (state of Pará)

These complex and well-organized civilizations could have had thousands of inhabitants. Some theorists suggest that the enormous biodiversity presently found in Amazonia, such as edible fruits, is a result of human ancestral presence in the region. Large scale geometric drawings (geoglyphs), found in the clayed soils of the state of Acre, may have been made in fields previous to the formation of forests.

During their long journeys, some groups planted seeds along the way, ensuring they would have food on their return.

Today ceramic pottery still follows the traditional indigenous culture found in Central Amazon before the 16th century.

26

Indigenous Peoples

Indigenous Lands

396 regions make up 98.5% of all indigenous areas in Brazil. This is 20.5% of the Brazilian Amazon.

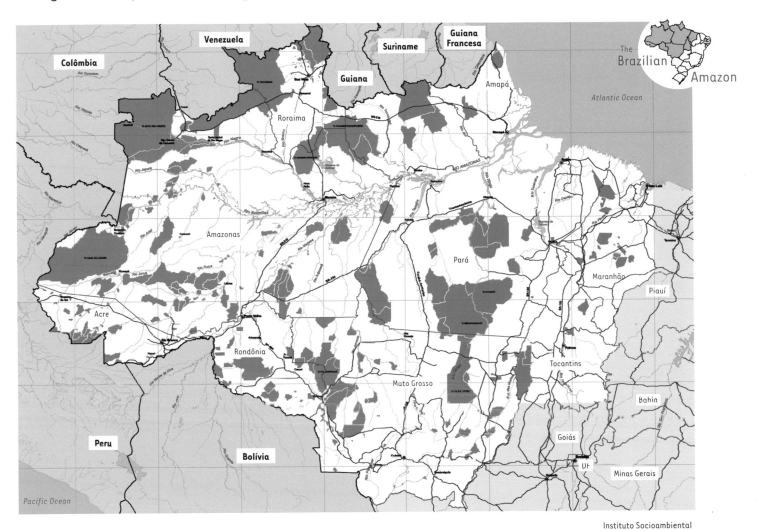

Instituto Socioambiental

● Indigenous Lands
— Principal Roads
◉ State Capital
○ Cities

Indigenous Peoples - The First Inhabitants

At present, there are 250 thousand indigenous peoples from 180 different cultures, each with its own language.

The indigenous people retain the ancestral knowledge of the forest and of the techniques they use to interact with the environment.

When the Portuguese first arrived, there were approximately 5 million indigenous people in Brazil. At present, 180 different tribes - each speaking a different language - reside in the Brazilian Amazon region.

The Zo'e People

Isolated Indigenous Peoples

Currently, there are approximately 70 isolated indigenous groups in the Brazilian Amazon that have had no contact with the outside world. We only know of these communities because of aerial surveillance. The current government policy focuses on protecting the lands of these indigenous peoples against external invasions; the isolated peoples are contacted only as a last resort.

The Zo'e

One of the last isolated indigenous tribes of the Brazilian Amazon, the Zo'é live in the northern Amazon municipality of Oriximiná, in the state of Pará.

In 1987, a group of Zo'é were visited by evangelical missionaries. This was the tribe's first contact with the outside world. They were exposed for the first time to viruses and bacteria causing illnesses such as the flu, conjunctivitis and pneumonia. Because their bodies had no defense against these germs, they became deathly ill. Only 133 people survived. The devastating epidemic required intervention from the National Indian Foundation and the Attorney-General.

In 2006, the Zo'é community of 238 people contracted malaria from loggers who had settled nearby. Federal officials and the National Indian Foundation (FUNAI) had to step in to deal with the resulting devastating epidemic.

The Zo'é wear the poturu, a wooden plug piercing the bottom lip, all their lives. The poturu, which they frequently wash in the rivers, distinguishes them from all other tribes and is part of their visual identity.

The Zo'é view the individual and the universe as one and the same. Similarly the individual is considered an integral part of the community. From their perspective, we are all part of the same being. There is no "we" or "my" in their language or in their worldview.

Indigenous House

An oca is the traditional name for the house of an indigenous person. Oca is a Tupi word. In fact, each indigenous language has its own word for house. It varies in shape, building material, size and utility, depending on each culture.

The Krahó in Tocantins organize their ocas in a circle. The Palikur in Amapá build theirs in a line along the river.

The Yanomami (between Brazil and Venezuela) typically build a huge structure that houses everyone — often over a hundred people live together.

Hammocks are hung inside the oca and residents agree among themselves where they will put their everyday belongings. There are usually bonfires lit inside the oca to keep the mosquitoes away or to warm the place on cold and humid nights. The ocas are generally dark, having no windows and few entrances.

Waurá's house (below) | Yanomami's house (right)

The sky at night on the 21st of July in the southern hemisphere.

The Amazon at night

Each tribe observes the sun, moon and stars closely—the appearance of certain constellations mark important seasonal changes. But instead of the mythical figures that westerners see, in the Amazon, the skies are populated with inhabitants of the forest, and it is the stories of each tribe that are told in the stars.

Wiranu - The Rhea Constellation

At the time the rhea constellation is totally visible at nightfall, the dry season begins in the forest. The rhea is the biggest bird in the Amazon and this ostrichlike bird represents abundance. For the Tembé Indians, when Wiranu can be seen at nightfall, it is harvest time.

Azim - The Seriema Constellation

The seriema is a cranelike bird with limited flight. When Azim, the seriema constellation, appears in the sky, it is the beginning of the dry season and time to harvest.

Tapi'i Hazywer - The Tapir's Chin Constellation

For westerners, this is the Taurus constellation. For the Tembé, when the chin of the tapir appears in the east it is a sign that the rainy season is about to begin.

Zauxihu Ragapaw - The Tortoise Constellation

When this starry tortoise crosses the northern Amazon sky, the Tembé know the rainy season has already begun.

Tapi'i - The Tapir Constellation

For the Tembé and many other tribes, the tapir is the most important animal in the forest. Most Brazilian Indians believe in the existence of a celestial tapir that wanders through the stars. This is why, instead of the Milky Way, there is the Tapir's Way.

Mainamy - The Hummingbird Constellation

Mainamy appears in the south in September. The Tembé celebrate the arrival of the hummingbird in the forest as well as in the night sky with festivities that include special dances and bathing in the river. With the appearance of Mainamy, the Tembé know that the dry season is coming to an end and that the rains will arrive soon.

Yar Ragapaw - The Canoe Constellation

The stars that form this constellation are the same ones that belong to parts of the constellations you might know as the Great Bear and the Little Lion. The Tembé's celestial canoe is situated in the northern sky.

The atmosphere in Amazonia is clear, pure and translucent. The horizon is limitless. At night, the stars illuminate the sky.

Extractive
Communities

We, the inhabitants of the interior of the country, just live on manioc flour and fish.

Thiago de Mello, Amazonian poet

There are over 30 thousand small communities in the rural areas of the Amazon. They live off the bounty of the Amazon basin as rubber tappers, nut and coconut grabbers, traditional fisherman, riverside inhabitants, small family producers, and quilombolas (descendants of 19th century runaway slaves who created their own communities).

Most communities consist of 5 to 200 families that reside on public lands or protected areas. They live on what they can harvest from the forest, from the planting of manioc and other crops, and from hunting and fishing.

There is very little paper currency circulated so bartering is still widely used in commercial operations.

Additionally, municipal public infrastructure is still insufficient in these rural zones. Long distances between settlements, combined with a lack of communication and transportation networks, condemn populations to almost absolute exclusion. As a result of deforestation the population is unable to guarantee its own subsistence.

Youngsters of the Forest

The population of Amazonia is predominantly young. They start working at a very early age in extractive activities, fishing, hunting and agriculture. Though these young people in the riverside communities have a different life-style from youngsters in other regions, they share with other Brazilian youth the same aspirations for material comfort and social status. These yearnings cause many Amazonian youth to migrate to the cities in search of better jobs or education.

Children of Oriximiná (a region of Trombetas river)

As they integrate into the urban culture, many begin to lose interest in the traditional knowledge. As a result, many youngsters no longer know how to make traditional remedies, or such important utensils as baskets, oars, fans or the palm cylinders used to express manioc juice.

Every day more and more communication technologies find their way into the forest. Already there is internet, group teleconferencing, boomboxes, cd players, and camcorders. The youth listen to both indigenous music and hip hop.

Education

Likewise, formal education in these communities is limited. Generally only children between seven and ten years of age go to school. Local radio is the major source of information. In search of work or further education more and more young people are migrating to urban centers. Because 47,5 % of the population of Amazonia is under 15 years of age, this growing migration poses serious challenges to preserving these indigenous cultures. Only 7,5% have access to complete secondary education.

The Women of the Forest

Women in the forest have a heavy workload. Besides sustaining the household, they look after their children, attend to health issues in the family, work in the fields, and are greatly involved in community activities such as festivities, processions and communal cleaning.

Their sexual life begins at an early age — in general, a woman has her first child at 16 years of age — and single mother rates are high. Families are numerous and children are born at home, with the help of midwives.

Women are the source of power and innovation within the communities. They organize mother clubs and frequently lead important social movements. Possessing strength and vision, women in the forest are the protagonists of their own stories.

Health

In these communities even a simple illness can escalate into a medical crisis because basic health care interventions are not available. The most common complaints are water-borne diarrhea, anemia, intestinal parasitosis, preventable and respiratory illnesses, lifestyle related articular and muscular ailments. Malaria, Leishmaniasis, dengue and yellow fever, tuberculosis and Hansen's disease are also frequently found in many areas.

High levels of malnutrition and infant mortality can be easily avoided with preventative measures, including immunizations, but the region is so vast and the communities so isolated that carrying out the doable is a great challenge.

Yet, in spite of all this, these people preserve the extensive traditional knowledge of Amazonia, including the management of its natural resources; their survival, after all, depends on the forest.

A Caboclo's house

Caboclo is the generic term used for all the traditional mestizo inhabitants of the Amazon.

Caboclos are a hospitable and convivial people, who live simple lives. In general, they purchase few consumer goods. Those few industrialized products caboclos do own are creatively recycled. Typically, a caboclo's house is made of straw and all utensils derive from the forest.

Flour Mill

The manioc root (maniva), or cassava, is the staple diet in the Amazon, and is a major source of carbohydrates. The proper way to process manioc is part of the region's millennial knowledge.

The bitter variety of manioc is poisonous when raw. However, once processed it becomes flour, starch, tapioca and tucupi, with multiple regional culinary uses. The "biju" is the Amazonian bread.

The Rubber Manufacturing

Latex is harvested from the rubber tree trunks, and taken to the manufacturing unit where the latex is smoked and dried.

Native to the Amazon, natural rubber underpinned an important development boom in the 19th century, when thousands of immigrants moved to the region to help harvest the latex. At that time, the industrial revolution was expanding and synthetic rubber had not yet been developed. Today, modern techniques transform the combination of latex and cotton into vegetable leather.

Positive Experiences

Pedagogy of Alternance

Based on an Alternance System, this educational process organizes classes by alternating periods at the education center (school) with periods in social, vocational and family settings. A number of schools follow different models of this concept. **www.unefab.org.br | fvpp@amazoncoop.com.br**

Children's Pastoral Care

This community organization has become a major force in the region, reaching out to and helping even the most remote communities in Brazil. They provide training for mothers to improve the health, nutrition and education of their children. **www.pastoraldacrianca.org.br**

IEPA - Institute for Scientific and Technological Resewarch of Amapá

In partnership with other government agencies and NGOs, IEPA leads the Land Pharmacy Project, which stimulates the sharing of knowledge of medicinal herbs and native plants among the communities. **www.iepa.ap.gov.br**

Other links
www.amazonia.fiocruz.br | www.butantan.gov.br

28

Fighting for the forest

The world often thinks of Amazonia as being an uninhabited forest. However, the region is populated by peoples and communities who have a profound knowledge of nature and a very practical approach to every situation. They fight to preserve their environment, their culture and their traditional life-style. Chico Mendes was one of the pioneers who created the networks of cooperation between the peoples of the forest. Supporting these communities is the most realistic strategy to assure a balanced and sustainable Amazonia and the preservation of its peoples.

Positive Experiences

GTA - Amazon Working Group

A network comprised of over 600 institutions throughout Amazonia. It was founded in 1992.
www.gta.org.br

COIAB - Brazilian Amazon Coalition of Indigenous Organizations

Comprised of 77 networks of tribes and Indigenous lands. **www.coiab.com.br**

CNS - National Rubber Trappers Network

Founded in 1985 by Chico Mendes, who created a new model for forest extractive reserves.
www.cnsnet.org.br

MIQCB - Interstate Movement of the Babaçu Coconut Breakers

Created at the end of the 20th Century by over 200 thousand women breakers from eastern Amazon.
www.miqcb.org.br

MONAPE - National Movement of Native Fisherman

Founded in 1988. Has obtained unemployment insurance for fishermen during the months when fish are reproducing.
monape@amazon.com.br

Others

Carajas Forum - www.forumcarajas.org.br
East Amazon Forum - www.faor.org.br
Mato Grosso Development Forum - www.formad.org.br
Front of Defense of Amazon - ceftbam@yahoo.com.br

Indigenous man at the Brazilian Parliament
Public protest against advancement of agrobusiness

Forest Economy

29

Today, forest related economy represents only 1% of the Brazilian Amazon's total economy

Nowadays, the market tends to be aligned with environmental, social and cultural values. Within this context, Amazonia, in particular, has captured the attention of conscientious consumers and companies, who detect business opportunities in the sustainable options for the development of the region.

Rendering the forest economy competitive yet sustainable in the face of current destructive production models and a rapidly advancing consumerism is a major challenge.

Values

This millennium, Amazonia's greatest challenge will be one of reconciliation. On the one hand Amazonia faces the development of an increasingly globalized society with its consumption habits. On the other hand, the environment that feeds us all, as well as the cultures of the forest peoples, whose ancestral wisdom, customs and traditional life-styles invite our respect and attention, must somehow be preserved.

Modern and technological development must be ethical and sustainable to ensure a balanced and sustainable future for Amazonia, its peoples, and the planet we live on.

Respect for and support of these peoples' survival and civil rights are prerequisites to adding value and competitiveness to the ancient knowledge as it is replicated in the modern world. We all need this wisdom!

Carmen Miranda red latex skirt and top — Alexandre Herchcovich collection

Investments

Amazonia offers significant investment opportunities, especially if modern technologies and concepts are applied to the immense — and not yet fully known — forest diversity.
Raw materials, forest derivatives, and traditional knowledge can have a competitive place in a market aligned with the future of the planet.

Bangle – Brazil chestnut bur with silver by Hilea Design

Consume sustainable products from Amazonia!

Felix Chair by Fernando Jeager

For more information

Experimental Projects Program
www.mma.gov.br/agroextrativismo

Mercado Amazônia
www.mercadoamazonia.org.br

Sustainable Bussiness Database
http://negocios.amazonia.org.br

Rainforest Alliance
www.ra.org

Forest Stewarship Council
www.fsc.org.br

Rural Territories Program
www.mda.gov.br/sdt

Slow Food Brasil
www.slowfoodbrasil.com

Bolsa Amazonia
www.bolsaamazonia.com.br

Sebrae Brasil
www.sebrae.com.br

Equator Initiative
www.undp.org/equatorinitiative

Ecotourism

Ecotourism is one of the greatest opportunities for the non-aggressive development of the Amazon. This beautiful and mysterious region attracts the world's curiosity. It has much to teach, and, above all, offers a deep personal experience of contact with the immensity of nature, and with a people who live their lives with a rare simplicity, kindness, and spontaneous joy.

Visit the Amazon and learn more about yourself and our world.

Ecotourism in the communities

Lakes Village
www.viverde.com.br/aldeia.html

Mamirauá Institute for Sustainable Development
www.mamiraua.org.br

Ethnotourism in the Alto Negro River
www.artebaniwa.org.br

Black Rocks
www.ecopore.org.br

Cristalino Park
www.cristalinolodge.com.br

Chapada das Mesas Park
www.turismo.ma.gov.br/pt/polos/chapada/

Jaú National Park
www.fva.org.br

Peabiru Institute
www.peabiru.org.br

Argonautas
www.argonautas.org.br

Jalapão State Park
www.conservation.org.br/onde/cerrado/index.php?id=166

National Parks and Reserves
www.icmbio.gov.br

Hostel in Mamirauá, Solimões river | Samaúma tree

30

Positive Initiatives

Thousands of sustainable initiatives in Amazonia, even though isolated and limited in support and resources, counterbalance the devastation that assails the region.

NGOs (non governmental organizations) and the network of social action groups do not aim to replace the government. Their role is to develop innovative initiatives and create awareness that can influence and direct governmental policies.
These institutions offer the communities support and services related to developmental and technological matters. They also exert social control by demanding transparency in the use of public resources and they pressure decision makers to act properly in causes they consider just.

The major setback these organizations face is a lack of resources. Many have almost no equipment and have a very limited staff. There are approximately twelve thousand NGOs in Amazonia, the majority of which have emerged from the urban areas. There are roughly one thousand organized social action groups in the rural areas.

Most NGOs and social action groups rely exclusively on volunteer work. 80% don't have computers and 50% don't have telephones.

Most of the international funding invested in environmental programs is funneled through the Brazilian government. Donors that send resources directly to NGOs demand transparency, and many NGOs undergo regular auditing.

Serious NGOs publish and divulge their programs and activities, as their source of income depends on credibility.

Support Brazilians in their efforts to protect the Amazon

Support the projects that are positive.

Amazonia Brasil Campaign

This campaign supports social and productive demands identified as urgent in the communities. It also promotes local experiments that support practical and real investments opportunities. Participation can be through partnerships or by direct contribution to a fund managed by a board of leaders with specialized technical advice. **www.amazoniabrasil.org.br**

Many groups to support

Indigenous Peoples

Ashaninka Apiwtxa Association

Brings together the Ashaninka people with other indigenous peoples and riverside communities of the Amazon River. This association focuses mainly on culture, music and the management of natural resources (agroecology). **www.apiwtxa.blogspot.com**

Indigenous Council of Roraima

Brings together a majority of the indigenous groups in the state of Roraima, located in northern Brazilian Amazonia. It has been a strong supporter of the rights of indigenous people. **www.cir.org.br**

Healthy Fruit Association | Wity Caty

The Wity Caty association is located in the Kraho and Timbira villages. It is a joint conservation/business venture seeking to create profitable small businesses for indigenous populations and small farmers through the sustainable extraction of native fruit pulps from the threatened Cerrado region. Fruits are harvested using traditional methods and processed in a coop factory and then sold to local and state markets. **www.trabalhoindigenista.org.br | projetos_frutos_cerrado.asp**

Hutukara Yanomami Association

Led by Davi Kopenawa, the association has been very active in denouncing biopiracy of ancestral knowledge. The organization is committed to the preservation of the Yanomami peoples, who continue to live much as they did for millennia, depending on the forest environment for their daily life. **hutukara@yahoo.com.br**

Kanindé Association of Ethnic and Environmental Defense

Is dedicated to promoting an ongoing dialogue between the urban culture and the indigenous people in the state of Rondonia. It develops and produces maps that depict the indigenous people's knowledge, customs and worldview. **www.kaninde.org.br**

Yawanawa Association

Formed by the Yawanawa people who live by the Gregório River, has introduced innovative clothing design based on traditional body painting. **www.yawanawa.com**

Alliance of the Peoples of the Roncador River

Unites the Wederã village residents that descend from the Xavante nation. The organization is committed to the conservation of natural resources, such as the wild pig that is an important part of their traditional diet. Their culture and ceremonies have been recorded in films, such as Darini. **www.wedera.blogspot.com**

Child and Youth

Uga Uga Agency for the Rights of Children and Adolescents

Is active in the city of Manaus and throughout the state of Amazonas. It promotes, among other initiatives, programs concerning family planning and the prevention of child labor. **www.agenciaugauga.org.br**

Matraca Agency for the Rights of Children and Adolescents

Is active in the city of São Luis and throughout the state of Maranhão. It promotes social development and human rights of youth in the region. **www.matraca.org.br**

Women of the Forest

Green Life Association of Amazonia

In the city of Silves, defends and preserves the local environment and culture while also working to improve the quality of life of local people, especially women. Much of AVIVE's work has focused on developing techniques for sustainable extraction of the Aniba plant, also known as pau-rosa, as well as other medicinal and aromatic native plant species. **www.avive.org.br**

Black Women's Institute

Produces radio programs and community events to promote the culture and social movements of black women in the state of Amapá.
www.portalafro.com.br / entities / imena.htm

Interstate Movement of the Babaçu Coconut Breakers

Brings together over 200,000 men and women in four states, to support the conservation of natural resources, in particular the babaçu palm tree, traditionally used in the production of flour and now in new products such as soap and oil. Additionally the organization is fighting for a national law that ensures free access to the forests for the babaçú gatherers and to halt the destruction of the babaçu palm tree, which is indispensable to the local economy. **www.miqcb.org.br**

Indigenous Women's Association of Southern Acre and Amazonas

Was formed to support the initiatives and the rights of female indigenous peoples in the southern region of the states of Acre and Amazonas.
www.sitoakure.blogspot.com

Quilombolas

Quilombos Communities Association of Maranhão

Is an organization that fights for the land rights of the quilombos - the communities of descendants of runaway slaves.
http://encontroquilombola_ma.uniblog.com.br

Quilombos Communities Association of Oriximiná

Created by the riverside communities of the Trombetas Rivers, in Pará, the association promotes the cultural heritage of former African slaves, fights to obtain their land titles and strives to develop sustainable management of natural resources. This group has inspired research on ethnobiology.
www.quilombo.org.br

Family Agroforestry

Association in the Settlement Areas of the State of Maranhão

Based in the capital city of São Luis, combines deep relationships in the local communities, traditional know-how and the latest agroecological techniques for sustainable farming (agro-biodiversity and agroforestry). One of ASSEMA's goals is to improve the production and value of the babaçu nut, a traditional crop with great economic potential because its oil has many uses, including natural health and skin care products.

www.assema.org.br

Ecological Farmers of the Amazon Cooperative

Located in northern Mato Grosso, a region severely affected by deforestation due to monoculture agriculture. The cooperative is made up of many small farmers dedicated to organic agriculture and sustainable farming.

www.bioagrepa.com

Apaflora - Alternative Producers Association

Is a successful initiative created by farmers in Ouro Preto d'Oeste, in the state of Rondônia. The association is committed to producing fruit and other crops in such a way that their impact on the forest will be minimal.

apaflora@ouronet.com.br

Apato Alternative Producers Association

Located in the deforestation region in northern Tocantins, promotes and supports sustainable farming, production and environmental conservation.

apatobico@uol.com.br

Reca Project

Association of Small-scale Agro-Silviculturists makes use of lands donated by the Brazilian government to colonies in1984 for small-scale agroforestry development in southeastern Amazonia. To do this, the group introduced a new "production model" that is sustainable, organic and based on partnerships or associations. RECA also implements other programs in the area pertaining to education, health and business management. **projetoreca@yahoo.com.br**

Agroforestry Research Group

Is dedicated to research and development of models of sustainable rural production in the Amazon, with the goal of conserving biodiversity. Their efforts combine a respect for traditional practices with a desire to maximize production. **www.pesacre.org.br**

Community Ecotourism

Aspac- Aldeia dos Lagos (Village of the Lakes)

Was the first community-based Ecotourism project in the Amazon region. It was built as part of Project Silves, whose mission is to develop community-based ecotourism in the Brazilian Amazon. ASPAC was in charge of the project and received technical support from WWF and was sponsored by the Austrian Government.
www.viverde.com.br / aldeia.html

Federation of Indigenous Organizations of the Alto Negro River

Is located in São Gabriel da Cachoeira, where approximately 90% of the population consists of indigenous peoples and their descendents. Most of the town is located on indigenous land and it is the only Brazilian municipality where four official languages are spoken. **foirn@uol.com.br**

Mamirauá Institute for Sustainable Development

Was founded by the researcher Márcio Ayres on a large tract of land by the Solimões River, in western Amazonas. This renowned science center is committed to research and development that will yield a long-term action plan for sustainability in partnership with the local population. The Institute's hostels also offer excellent accommodations for visitors.
www.mamiraua.org.br

Environmental Argonauts of the Amazon

Based in Belém, the organization promotes various sustainable development initiatives through tourism and community events. **www.argonautas.org.br**

Community Organization

The Association of the Fishermen of Bailinque

Is located in the Bailinque Archipelago, at the mouth of the Amazon River. The association has helped create schools offering classes in environmental studies, has helped establish local radio stations, and has helped develop community products. The local community, which practices sustainable fishing methods, has benefited economically from this association's efforts.
www.bailique.blogspot.com

Preservation and Development Group (GDP)

Is a pioneer community-management initiative committed to the preservation of lakes and their fish stocks. Their programs rely on volunteer environmental agents, a type of involvement that is becoming increasingly popular in the Amazon today.
gpd@eganet.com.br

Support Small Projects!

Xingu Fund

Supported by interested financial institutions, promotes rural development projects in the communities located between the Xingu River and the BR 163 Highway, in the state of Mato Grosso. This initiative's objective is to protect and restore the river sources and forest galleries. The fund finances an environmental campaign conducted by Centro Vida Institute, Socioambiental Institute and others organizations. **www.yikatuxingu.org.br**

Dema Fund

Was created with resources generated by the sale of illegal timber seized by the government. It is managed by the FASE organization and supports environmental and conservation projects. It has greatly contributed to community empowerment by being one of the main supporters of community radio stations.
www.fase.org.br/_fundo_dema/

Rio Negro's Social Market

Is an important science ethnical center that supports sustainable development alternatives as well as offering commercial models for the traditional communities on the Negro River.
www.fva.org.br

Luthier School and Workshop

Works with young people in the suburbs of Manaus and in rural communities. Computers are an integral part of its programs. The school searches for new alternative materials for the musical instruments the students construct and is committed to the use of certified wood in everything they produce.
www.oela.org.br

Preserve, Work and Live Foundation

Is located in the central region of the Transamazonian Highway. The organization works with the people who settled in this region in the 1970s, striving to eliminate practices that cause deforestation, e.g., the use of fire to clear the land. They support the pedagogy of alternance school system.
fvpp@amazoncoop.com.br

The Digital Connection

Navegar Project

Provides Web connectivity to riverine communities. The project uses a boat that holds a multimedia laboratory and has a satellite antenna for internet connection. By offering internet access as well as training in photography and video making, the project has improved the quality of life in the Bailique region. A renowned Brazilian filmmaker manages the Navegar project. **www.navegaramazonia.org.br**

Video in Villages

Is a cultural production that enables young people to make and edit their own videos. It is an important initiative of the indigenous peoples of the Brazilian Amazon. **www.videonasaldeias.org.br**

Nortão Cultural Center

Is run by the Rural Workers Trade Union In Mato Grosso. With the use of digital equipment donated by the Ministry of Culture, this organization publishes regional newspapers, videos and CDs involving many local artists and communities. **www.strlrv.blogspot.com**

Health and Happiness

31

A primary objective of Health and Happiness is to promote and support a system of participatory and sustainable community development. In turn, this should contribute to the improvement of public policies, the quality of life and the exercise of citizenship.

Since 1987, PSA has been providing community development services to extractive communities along the Amazon, Tapajós and Arapiuns rivers, and to the rural areas of the municipalities of Santarém, Belterra and Aveiro, in the western region of the state of Pará. Beginning in 2003, the organization started to gradually expand the areas in which it operates, now serving 143 localities, and benefiting over 30,000 people.

The organization's objective is to support sustained community development through integrated and participatory management of social and environmental projects.

Starting with the most pressing needs, based on the input of residents, Health and Happiness seeks out simple solutions adapted to the communities' available resources.

An interdisciplinary team of doctors, agronomists and educators visit the communities regularly. The team coordinates the work of various community organizations so that the activities they implement addresses all aspects of the people's lives: health, agro-forestry production and management, income generation, education, art and culture, public communication and participatory research. Issues related to gender and the special needs of children and adolescents are an important part of the process.

A small touring circus that includes a radio, a TV and the "Mocorongo" newspaper - all of which are produced by the youth of the forest - is an integral part of the Health and Happiness support services.

The lessons learned working with one community often carries over to others. Thus an important part of what the Health and Happiness Project has accomplished is the construction of well-adapted and demonstrative social technologies that have a low cost and high impact.

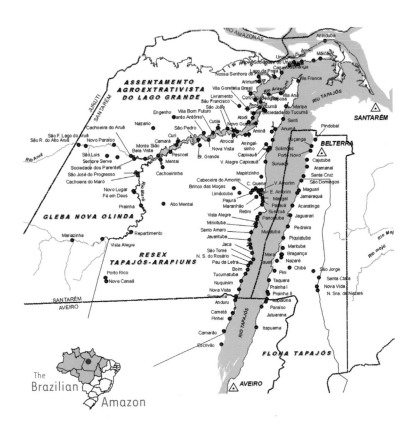

Because these systems can be implemented in different areas and contexts, Health and Happiness currently receives increasing requests to advise governmental and non-governmental institutions in and beyond the Amazon region.

The challenge now is to change the scale of work and universalize the successful experiences.

150 communities, involving around 30,000 beneficiaries.

www.saudeealegria.org.br

**The Integrated and
Development Programs**

- Community organization
  and management

- Community Health

- Education, Culture
  and Communication

- Forest Economy

Instead of 'internationalizing' the Amazon, let's 'amazonize' the world.

GTA Network

The GTA Network (Amazonian Work Group) was created in 1992, and has 602 affiliated entities in nine stawtes of the region. They are organizations of various sizes; most of them small and linked to communities of forest people, as well as environmentalists, human rights movements and technical support. Since their first activities at the United Nations World Conference for the Environment and Development, held in Brazil, they have attempted to demonstrate the importance of the inhabitants of the forest and their knowledge for the future of the Amazon.

www.gta.org.br

Amazônia Brasil
Project

www.amazoniabrasil.org.br

Amazônia Brasil is a multicultural program that gathers together a wealth of knowledge about the Amazonian region, with all its inherent diversity, potential and contradictions. It presents the local communities, forest peoples and innovative projects; portraying the Amazon from the viewpoint of those who live and work there along with possible and realistic solutions with a variety of approaches and objectives.

This is not just a program "about" the region; it is more an exhibition "from" the region.

Put on by the Projeto Saúde e Alegria - Health and Happiness Project (PSA) and the Grupo de Trabalho Amazônico – Amazon Working Group (GTA), with the Executive Direction of Fare Arte, the exhibition represents more than 610 non-governmental organizations (NGOs), social movements and forest community leaders. It is also the result of extensive consultation with specialists, as well as partnerships with research institutions and governmental co-operation in developing and implementing positive public policies for the region.

Objectives

- To present a realistic and current vision of the Brazilian Amazon and its communities to the general public;
- To increase the general level of awareness and answer questions concerning the Amazon as well as our global environment;
- To generate improvements in the existing social and sustainable development initiatives, and to strengthen traditional communities as part of a realistic strategy for the region's future;
- To make known the co-operation among NGOs, the government, and national and international private sectors;
- To promote self sustaining economies and sustainable business initiatives in the Amazon region by promoting their products;
- To broaden the spectrum of those directly involved in ongoing qualitative processes of co-operation and provide continued support for joint venture programs;
- To strengthen both national and local initiatives for the responsible development of the Amazon in Brazil.

In **Amazônia Brasil** exhibit, the visitor will be transported to the heart of the forest through gigantic panels and photos, audiovisuals and installations that re-create the multifaceted Amazonian environment, its contradictions, biodiversity, peoples, villages and cities. And more... the Cultural Program includes symposiums, lectures, shows, photo exhibitions.

Design, Fashion and Sustainable Economy exhibit presents a landscape of contemporary Brazilian design and will present the diversity and quality of Brazilian leading designers, stylists and companies from the Amazon region. It introduces raw materials with emphasis on fair commerce, sustainable development and social responsibility.

Climate Change & Tropical Forests shows the relation between tropical forests and climate change, bringing together the latest scientific information on the subject and its impact on the planet. From the vantage point of the outer space and diving down into the forest, visitors will experience the role of the Amazon region in the global carbon and humidity cycle, and learn about the amazing functions of a "green ocean".

Mercado Amazônia - Sustainable opportunities in Amazonia

This initiative promotes community products as well as sustainable economic and social investment opportunities in the nine states comprised by the Brazilian Amazon. Currently, there are over 150 eco-businesses investment opportunities in the region. For further information, visit **www.mercadoamazonia.org.br.**

Amazônia Brasil in the Classroom

This project focuses on the creation of a parallel curriculum about Amazonia for 1st to 9th grades. Among other activities, the initiative includes lectures, teacher education workshops, art classes and exchange programs with students and representatives of Amazonia's communities.

The Peoples of the Forest Cultural House - An interactive space for the peoples of Amazonia

The Peoples of the Forest Cultural Center, in São Paulo, is the culmination of the Amazônia Brasil program. It will be a major cultural and exchange center, where peoples of the forests, the urban public and NGOs of the Brazilian Amazon will be represented, and investment opportunities in sustainable projects and products will be divulged.

32

Celebrating Amazonia

The Amazonian culture is rich in music, dance, visual arts and stories.

The Parintins Festival is the most popular of all festivities that abound throughout the region. The festival takes place in an island in the State of Amazonas, and attracts thousands of people every year. The entire town of Parintins splits into two teams; a blue team called Garantido, and a red one called Caprichoso. Each one is lead by an ox, dressed in the color of the team.

The ethnic and cultural diversity in Amazonia is transformed into beauty and creativity; this is just one example of the cultural power that resides in the planet's largest forest.

Last Call

You are invited to enter the world of the Brazilian Amazon and to assume your responsibility, as you learn about the ethical development alternatives in the region.

Share what you learn — visit the websites, participate in the events, buy the books and the products. But verify the origin of the products you buy so that you can support the existing but endangered Brazilian experiences.

Only by getting involved can you help strengthen these pioneering projects and create a new transformative consciousness.
Your actions are helping to determine the Amazon's future.

Learn more: www.amazoniabrasil.org.br

Amazônia Brasil Project

General Direction: Eugenio Scannavino Neto | Amazônia Brasil & PSA
Executive Direction: Fare Arte
Art Direction, Exposition and Book Design: Gringo Cardia | Mesosfera
Production Coordination: Mesosfera (Gringa Cardia) | Fare Arte
Graphic Design Coordination: Gleise Cruz
Graphic Design Assistants: Carolina Vaz and Gabriel Caymmi
Design and Fashion Director: Debora Laruccia | Hilea
Content and Research Coordination: José Arnaldo de Oliveira
Scientific Data and Research Assistant: Gloria Malavoglia
Data & Communication Coordination: Isabel Gnaccarini
Data & Communication Assistant: Janaina Pissinato

Set Design Team

Set Design NY: Mina Quental, Bernard Heimburger,
Renata Pittigliani, Joana Aronovich, Marina Felix and Mariana Ribas
Graphic Design Assistants: Flavia Castro and Rico Villarouca
Videos: Wallace Cardia and Marcia Medeiros
Video Research: Antonio Venancio
Soundtrack: Juno Holmrich, Ricky Villas Boas and Wallace Cardia
Lighting Designer: Carlos Lafert
Lighting Designer Assistant: Julio Cesar Katona

A project of

www.amazoniabrasil.org.br

Executive Direction and Information

www.farearte.com.br

R. Flórida, 1821 cj. 32
04565-906 | São Paulo
SP | BRAZIL
+55 11 5102 4396

Fare Arte Team

General Coordination and Fundraising: Anna Claudia Agazzi
Executive Direction and Production Coordination: Alvise Migotto
Director's Assistant Manager: Monica Torres
Institutional Coordination: Malu Ramos
Cultural Agenda: Andrea Branco
Production Coordination: Cynthia Macedo
Production Assistant: Mariana Nicoletti

Sponsored by

Support

Institutional support

Presented by

www.saudeealegria.org.br

www.gta.org.br

Content collaborators in Brazil

Ashoka Empreendedores Sociais Brasil-Paraguai
ASSEMA - The Association of Land Distribution
in the State of Maranhao
Avina Foundation
Chico Mendes Institute of Biodiversity Conservation
CI - Conservation International
CNS - Julio Barbosa
COIAB - Coordination of the Indigenous Organizations
of the Brazilian Amazon
Local Communities of Santarem and Pedro Pantoja
Ethos Institute
FLONA - Tapajos National Forest - Daniel Cohen
FVA -Vitória Amazônica Foundation | Alternative
Economical Programs
Greenpeace Brasil
GTA - Amazon Working Group
IBAMA - Brazilian Institute for Environment and Natural
Renewable Resources
IMAZON - Amazon Institute of People and the Environment |
Laboratório de Geoprocessamento e Sensoriamento Remoto
INPA - National Institute for Amazonian Research | MCT
INPE - National Institute for Space Research | MCT
CPTEC | Proarco Program | Panamazonia Project
IPAM - Institute of Environmental Research
ISA - Socio-Environmental Institute
LBA - Large Scale Biosphere-Atmosphere Project
in the Amazon
Mamirauá Institute for Sustainable Development | MCT
Manaustur - Pilot Program for the Protection
of the Brazilian Rainforests | MMA
MCT - Ministry of Science and Technology of Brazil
MMA - Ministry of Environment of Brazil
MPEG - Emilio Goeldi Museum of Pará | MCT
Prefeitura de Boa Vista
Prefeitura de Santarém
ProVárzea
SBF - Secretaria de Biodiversidade
e Florestas | Núcleo de Geoprocessamento | MMA
SBPC - Brazilian Society for the Progress of Science
Secretaria de Cultura do Estado do Amazonas
SUFRAMA - Superintendência da Zona Franca
de Manaus | Coordenação Geral de Comunicação Social
UFAM - Universidade Federal do Amazonas | Faculdade
de Ciências Agrárias
UNDP - United Nations Development Program

WWF - World Wildlife Fund Brasil
Ecological and Economic Zoning Plan | MMA

Photos

Special Credits
Araquém Alcântara - www.terrabrasilimagens.com.br,
www.araquem.com.br
Caetano Scannavino Filho - caetano@saudeealegria.org.br
Fábio Colombini - www.fabiocolombini.com.br
Luis Cláudio Marigo - www.lcmarigo.com.br
Luiz Estumano | Interfoto - www.interfoto.com.br
Paulo Santos | Interfoto - www.interfoto.com.br
Renato Soares - www.renatosoares.com.br
Rodrigo Petrella - www.rodrigopetrella.com
Rosa Gauditano | Studio R - www.studior.com.br

Agência Brasil
Agência de Florestas do Estado do Amazonas
André Villas Boas | ISA
Andrea Branco
Anselmo D'Affonseca | INPA
Antônio Donato Nobre
Arquivo Programa LBA
Arquivo PSA
Augusto Pereira
Banco de Imagens ProVárzea/Ibama - L.C. Marigo
Carline Piva
Carlos Penteado
Clóvis Miranda | Manaustur
Emiliano Mancuso
Euzivaldo Queiroz | Suframa
Fabiana Leite | Manaustur
Fernando Marques | AE
Francisco Felipe Xavier Filho | INPA
Greenpeace
Ibama Collection
João Ramid
Josivaldo Cesar Modesto | Mamirauá Institute
for Sustainable Development | MCT
Juliana Pazuello | Suframa
Kaliandra Sá
Laboratório de Fisiologia Comportamental
e Evolução - LFCE | INPA
Manaustur Collection
Marcela Beltrão
Marcos Amend | Mamirauá Institute for Sustainable

Development | MCT
Mauricio de Paiva | FVA
MMA - Ministry of Environment of Brazil
Orib Ziedson | Prefeitura de Boa Vista (RR)
Patricia Charvet-Almeida
Paulo Artaxo
Pio Figueroa
SEC-AM | A. NETO
Sergio Oliveira Filho | Manaustur
Stock.xchng (web)
Fundação Instituto Floresta Tropical | FFT

Acknowledgements

Adalberto Luis Val
Adhara Scannavino
Adilson Vieira - GTA
Alexandre Rivas | Piatam Project
Alfredo Leoni
Ana Anjos
Ana Paula Soares
Ana Prates
Antonio Manzi
Benki Ashaninka
Beto Lopes |GTA
Caetano Scannavino
Caetano Scannavino Filho
Caio Magri
Carlos e Livia Dantas de Carvalho
Carlos Roberto Bueno
Carolina Ramos
Caroline Donatti
Catarina da Silva Motta
Celia Cruz
Célio Magalhães
Charles R. Clement
Davi Said Aidar
Davi Yanomami
Deus
Eduardo Trazzi
Egídio Arai
Erika Schloemp
Fabiano Lopez da Silva
Fernando Rocchetti dos Santos
Gloria M. Scannavino
Hugo Guimarães de Mesquita
Ima Vieira

Ivo Galindo
Jackson Colares
João Carlos Capobianco
João Fortes
Joice Santos
Jorge Costa Neves
José Gomes
José Ximenes
Josivaldo Cesar Modesto
Juliana Dantas Pazuello
Kátia Regina
Leonel Del Prete
Liliana Cerri Agazzi
Luis Lopes
Luis Maurano
Luiz Andrade da Silva
Luiz Antonio de Oliveira
Luis Mansueto
Marcelo Bassols Raseira
Marcia Gama
Marcia Munick M. Cabral
Maria Nazareth Paula da Silva
Mario Agazzi
Muriel Saragoussi
Newton Falcão
Nilson Gabas Junior | Emilio Goeldi Museum of Pará
Oded Grajew
Pamela Hartigan
Paulo Augusto Escada
Paulo Roberto Martini
PSA Team: Abaré Team, Caetano Scannavino,
Magnolio Oliveira, Elaine Pisa, Ronaldo Santana,
Fabio Penna, Fabio Tozzi, Lucia Oliveira and Ricardo Folhes
Raquel Telles de Moreira Sampaio
Renato Cintra
Renato Prado dos Santos
Ricardo Braga-Neto
Ricardo Verucci
Ricardo Young
Rosangela Alanis
Rubens Gomes - OELA
Sylvia Garantizado
Vanderli Tadei
Vera Maria Almeida-Val
Willian Magnusson
Yázigi Internexus